Scholastic

LITERACY PLACE

TABLE OF CONTENTS

UNIT 4

Hit Series

TABLE OF CONTENTS

TABLE OF CONTENTS

UNIT
6

Community Quilt

Hit Series

Visit a
Publishing Company

A creative idea can grow into a series.

What a Character!

Hit series often have memorable characters.

SERIES:
The Baby-sitters Club

CHARACTER:
Jackie Rodowsky

• seven years old
• red hair, red cheeks, freckles
• old grin, with one tooth missing

A Series for Everyone

There are many different kinds of series.

ANTWON BUTLER
age 8

LITTLE HOUSE IN THE BIG WOODS

Long-Running Hits

Some series last for years and years.

Trade Books

The following books accompany this *Hit Series* SourceBook.

Realistic Fiction

Go Fish

by Mary Stolz
illustrated by
Pat Cummings

Social Studies Nonfiction

...If You Lived at the Time of the Great San Francisco Earthquake

by Ellen Levine
illustrated by
Pat Grant Porter

Informational Fiction

Scholastic's The Magic School Bus® Inside the Human Body

by Joanna Cole
illustrated by
Bruce Degen

Newbery Honor
Classic Fiction

Ramona Quimby, Age 8

by Beverly
Cleary
illustrated by
Alan Tiegreen

Hit series often have memorable characters.

What a Character!

Travel along a time line and meet some of your favorite characters. Then board The Magic School Bus with the unforgettable Ms. Frizzle.

Discover how author Joanna Cole and illustrator Bruce Degen create their popular Magic School Bus series.

Join Jessi on a baby-sitting job that fizzles instead of sizzles.

WORKSHOP 1

Use your imagination to create a new character for your favorite series.

SERIES:
The Baby-sitters Club

CHARACTER:
Jackie Rodowsky

• seven years old
• red hair, red cheeks, freckles
• big grin, with one tooth missing
    Shea and Archie

A CENTURY of Hits

They're in books, in movies, on TV, and on your computer screen. They're almost everywhere you look. Who are they? Your favorite characters!

1900 1910 1920

1902

Peter Rabbit

The Tale of Peter Rabbit hopped to fame as the best-selling children's book ever.

1924

The Boxcar Children

All aboard! The author longed to live in a caboose. She couldn't, but she created characters who did.

Batman

Batman didn't start out with his trademark cape and costume. At first, the artist drew him with stiff bat's wings and a red outfit!

1939

Madeline

There are actually two Madelines. One is the French school girl. The other is . . . the author's wife!

Lassie

A dog named Pal was the first Lassie. The latest Lassie is Pal's great-great-great-great-great-grandson.

1943

1950

Ramona

The world's most famous pest lives on Klickitat Street, a real street in Portland, Oregon. The author grew up just a few blocks away.

1930   1940   1950

1931

Babar

Babar began in France as a bedtime story. The well-dressed elephant now stars worldwide in books, on TV, and on cassette.

1950

Charlie Brown

The *Apollo 10* astronauts named their command ship *Charlie Brown*. Naturally, they called the lunar module . . . *Snoopy!*

1969

Kermit

Kermit started out being a lizard! He was changed into a frog just before he made his bow on *Sesame Street*.

1963

Encyclopedia Brown

The boy detective speaks only English. But his adventures have been translated into 14 different languages!

1962

Clifford

Talk about big! This red dog isn't just a book and video. He's a giant balloon in New York's Thanksgiving Day Parade.

1960

1970

1963

Amelia Bedelia

Who but Amelia Bedelia would put sponges in sponge cake? The author, that's who! She tried out *all* of Amelia's recipes.

1971

Chapulin Colorado

The "red grasshopper" leaped over the border from Mexico. Now he struts his stuff on Spanish-language TV channels here.

Carmen Sandiego

Where is Carmen Sandiego? Millions of players track her across their computer screens. They chase her on TV, too!

1985

1988

Iktomi

Iktomi is a trickster in the folklore of the Lakota people. He's so tricky that he goes by at least 10 different names!

1981

Julian

Where do stories come from? Author Ann Cameron got some of hers from the true adventures of her friend, Julian DeWetts.

1980

1990···▶

1986

The Baby-sitters Club

Call these baby-sitters and what do you get? The country's most popular middle-grade series.

1986

Ms. Frizzle

The Friz drove the Magic School Bus right off the page and onto your television screen.

1991

The Time Warp Trio

These three have the time of their lives as they warp from the Stone Age to the Old West and back. Who knows where they'll be going next!

Scholastic's **The Magic School Bus**®

Television Script

AWARD WINNING

Books

from

Scholastic's

The Magic School Bus Hops Home

a TV Script by Jocelyn Stevenson

illustrated by **Nancy Stevenson**

based on **The Magic School Bus**® book series

by **JOANNA COLE** and **BRUCE DEGEN**

FROM THE DESK OF MS. FRIZZLE

Time for another adventure on The Magic School Bus!

This week, we're studying habitats—the places where animals live. Wanda wanted to do her part, so she brought her bullfrog Bella to school. Wanda tried to make a perfect classroom habitat for Bella, but Bella had other ideas. When Arnold opened a window, Bella hopped out!

Ms.Frizzle

Wanda

Dorothy Ann

Keesha

Phoebe

Arnold

Tim

Ralphie

Carlos

Liz the Lizard

THE MAGIC SCHOOL BUS
HOPS HOME

CHARACTERS

WANDA	PHOEBE
ARNOLD	KEESHA
RALPHIE	CARLOS
TIM	DOROTHY ANN
MS. FRIZZLE	LIZ THE LIZARD

[INTERIOR OF MS. FRIZZLE'S CLASSROOM. DAYTIME.]

WANDA

Arnold!! Bella's gone!!!

ARNOLD

Gone? Where?

WANDA

Out the window! Arnold, did you
open it?

ARNOLD

[shakes his head innocently] Well yes,
but—I thought she could use some
air.

[Everyone runs to the window to look out. RALPHIE comes
up to ARNOLD.]

RALPHIE

Nice one, Arnold.

[WANDA wanders grief–stricken around the room.]

WANDA

Why would Bella leave? Why? Why? Why? It's so perfect here!

[TIM holds up the duck mug in one hand and the beanbag frog in the other.]

TIM

Maybe she needed more from her habitat than a duck mug and a beanbag shaped like a frog …

[WANDA takes the mug and beanbag away from TIM and puts them with all of Bella's other toys.]

WANDA

Tim, those were her special things!

[WANDA faces everyone.]

WANDA

I've got to find her!

[Then she grabs ARNOLD, who's trying to sneak back to his desk.]

WANDA

And you've got to help me.

[She grabs the beanbag frog.]

WANDA

Ms. Frizzle? Could we be excused to go look for Bella?

[MS. FRIZZLE raises an eyebrow at LIZ, who starts to pack up her hammock.]

MS. FRIZZLE

That's an excellent idea, Wanda! In fact …

CUT TO means to quickly change from one scene to another.

[MS. FRIZZLE'S dragonfly earrings start to spin.]

MS. FRIZZLE

… why don't we make it a …

[The kids run for the door.]

ARNOLD

Oh no!

KIDS

Field trip!!!

[CUT TO: INTERIOR OF MAGIC SCHOOL BUS. DAYTIME. MS. FRIZZLE is at the wheel. WANDA sits right behind her, clutching her beanbag frog, worrying. LIZ is stringing up her hammock. ARNOLD climbs on the bus and takes a seat.]

ARNOLD

I think I should have stayed home today.

WANDA

I think Bella should have stayed home today! How are we ever going to find her? She could have hopped anywhere!

MS. FRIZZLE

Not exactly anywhere, Wanda. As I always say, to find a frog, be a frog.

[MS. FRIZZLE starts pushing buttons on the dashboard.]

ARNOLD

Be a frog?!! Oh no! Does that
mean we're going to …

[CUT TO: EXTERIOR OF MAGIC SCHOOL BUS.
Through some funny changes, it shrinks to the size of a
very large bullfrog—complete with frogs' legs. Now it is
a bus/frog.]

ARNOLD

… shrink …

[The BUS/FROG hops past an amazed cat, toward rear of
school, and out of frame.]

KIDS

[OFF] Whoooaaaaaaaaahhhhhh!!!

[CUT TO: INTERIOR OF BUS/FROG.
The kids look as if they're riding a bucking bronco,
and RALPHIE doesn't like it.]

RALPHIE

Hey, take it easy.

[LIZ is hanging onto her hammock for dear life. WANDA
and ARNOLD peer anxiously out the window, as the
landscape rises and falls with each hop. MS. FRIZZLE
sings to herself, happy as a clam.]

MS. FRIZZLE

[humming] "Where oh where has
my little frog gone. …"

[WANDA leans forward—suddenly excited!]

WANDA

Ms. Frizzle, maybe Bella just
hopped out to find some food!

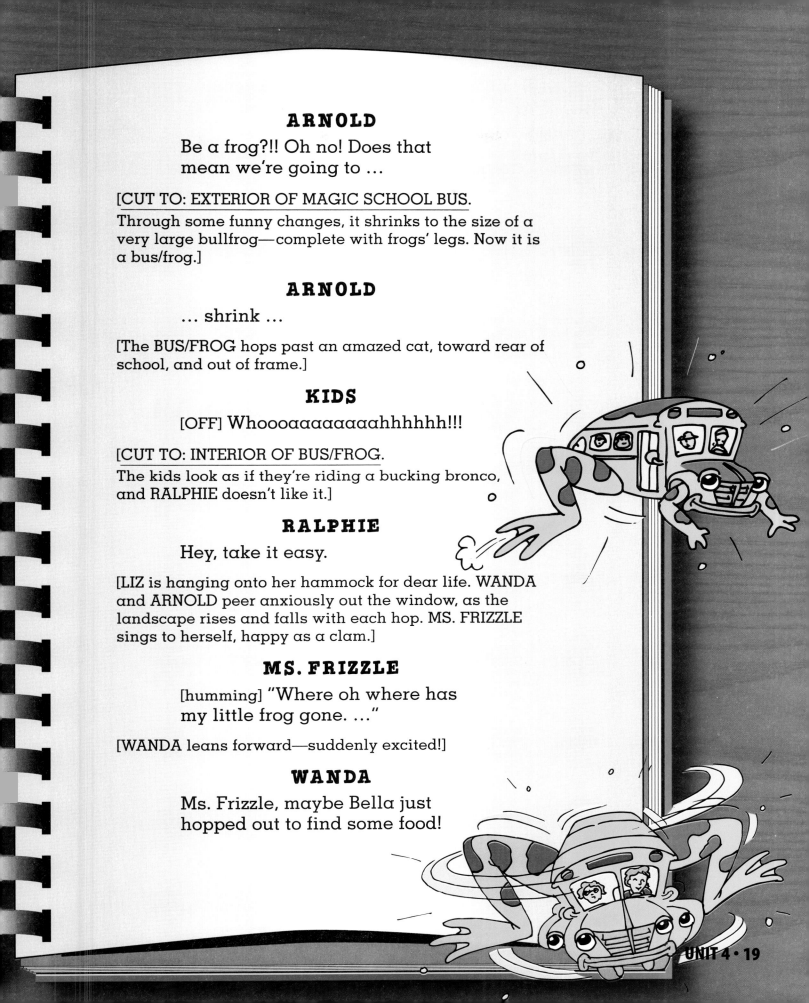

SHOT OF means a picture taken by the camera.

[SHOT OF RALPHIE who dizzily watches the landscape go by.]

RALPHIE

Food? Who can think of food at a time like this?

[SHOT OF MS. FRIZZLE, who smiles.]

MS. FRIZZLE

That is definitely a speculation worth consideration, Wanda!

ARNOLD

What kind of food? Cornflakes? Malloblasters?

WANDA

Bugs!

PHOEBE

[gasps] Eeww!!

[SHOT OF KEESHA, who's enjoying this.]

KEESHA

Maybe we should hop to the nearest bug habitat to have a look!

MS. FRIZZLE

What do you say, class?

[SHOT OF RALPHIE clutching his stomach.]

RALPHIE

Uh, Ms. Frizzle, do we have to hop?

[EXTERIOR. CLEARING.
We see a clearing complete with birds, a dead log, a few trees, and low growing plants and bushes. BUS/FROG hops into frame, landing beside log. BUS/FROG stops and the door opens.]

MS. FRIZZLE

Everybody out!

[SHOT OF the kids who slowly climb out of BUS/FROG and look around. LIZ stumbles out, dragging her hammock behind her. WANDA pushes past.]

WANDA

[calling] Bella! Bella! Where are you?? Belllaaaaahhhh!!!

[ARNOLD cringes from the volume of her voice.]

ARNOLD

Wanda! Quiet! You'll scare her away!

WANDA

[frustrated] Thanks to you, she's already away, Arnold. The question is where!

[Before another argument can start, a very big grasshopper hops by. MS. FRIZZLE scoops LIZ (with hammock) up into her arms and hops onto the grasshopper's back.]

MS. FRIZZLE

Hop along, class! Two by two, please!!

[Kids hop after MS. FRIZZLE, all except for RALPHIE, who's still feeling a little ill.]

A WIDE SHOT is a picture that shows a wide area.

RALPHIE

Thanks, but I'll wa-a-alk!!!

[A beetle scuttles between RALPHIE'S legs, taking him with it.]

RALPHIE

Whoa!!

[WIDE SHOT. Top of the log. MS. FRIZZLE and LIZ get off their grasshopper. The kids scramble up after her, dodging bugs. The place is crawling with them!]

CARLOS

Hey, this place is crawling with frog food!

[RALPHIE gets dumped by his beetle.]

RALPHIE

Oooff! [moans] Do you have to keep talking about food?

[MS. FRIZZLE helps him up.]

MS. FRIZZLE

Sorry, Ralphie, but food is one of the things all plants and animals need from their habitat.

[WANDA bears down on ARNOLD.]

WANDA

So, here's the food, Arnold. Where's Bella?

[ARNOLD lifts up leaves, fungi, moss looking for BELLA.]

ARNOLD

I'm looking … I'm looking.

SFX means sound effects.

[He parts some leaves on a branch and finds himself face to face with a cat.]
[SFX: CAT'S MEOW.]

ARNOLD

Yikes! I'm running!

[SHOT OF MS. FRIZZLE as she walks over to the cat.]

MS. FRIZZLE

[delighted] Oh look! It's a Felis Catus!

[BUS/FROG hops into frame and kids make a mad dash into it.]

KIDS

Hurry, hurry! Go, go! Let's get out of here!

[MS. FRIZZLE strolls back to BUS/FROG as the cat looks at her, confused.]

MS. FRIZZLE

But this is an excellent opportunity to study the behavior of cats!

KIDS

Ms. Frizzle!!

[CUT TO: INTERIOR OF BUS/FROG. DAYTIME.
MS. FRIZZLE steps into BUS/FROG and sits down and closes the bus door. She punches a button or throws a lever.]

MS. FRIZZLE

Here we go!

[CUT TO: EXTERIOR OF BUS/FROG.
The cat pounces, but BUS/FROG shoots up and out of the frame just in time.]

MS. FRIZZLE

[OFF] Waaaahoooooooooooooo!!!

[BUS/FROG lands in a tree.]
[CUT TO: INTERIOR OF BUS/FROG.
WANDA looks out window. She can't believe it.]

WANDA

We're in a tree??!?

[CARLOS tries to comfort her.]

CARLOS

Don't worry, Wanda. It's just a little
mis-hop.

ALL KIDS

Carlos!

[The kids look out and find themselves staring at a squirrel
family, which stares back. LIZ comes out from under the
seat and takes a look.]

MS. FRIZZLE

Not a mis-hop, Carlos. A tree is a
wonderful habitat!

[She takes them all off BUS/FROG.]
[CUT TO: EXTERIOR OF BUS/FROG. DAYTIME.
BUS/FROG is parked dangerously next to a hole in the tree
where some squirrels have made their nest. The kids
balance uncertainly on the branches. We see the cat
stalking down below.]

DOROTHY ANN

According to my research, it is a
perfect place for squirrels and birds!

[Bird tweets and flies by. Squirrels scamper down the trees.]

KEESHA

[looking down at cat] Yeah, it gives them a safe place away from cats to build their nests.

[One of the squirrels moves to reveal baby squirrels.]

PHOEBE

Oh look! Baby squirrels!

[WANDA is bursting with frustration.]

WANDA

But I don't want baby squirrels! I want Bella. And there's not enough space for her here. There's no food. Besides, where would she put her swimming pool?

[RALPHIE points to a limb of the tree.]

RALPHIE

I don't know. How about over there?

WANDA

Very funny, Ralphie.

[She looks up. Grabbing ARNOLD, she starts to climb.]

WANDA

Come on, Arnold. Let's see if we can see her.

ARNOLD

[hesitating] But Wanda …

[SFX: CREAKING BRANCH.]
[WANDA suddenly sees something below hopping away. Is it a frog?]

WANDA

There she is! Look! Bella! Bellllaaahh!

[She pulls ARNOLD after her.]

ARNOLD

No wait—Wanda!

WANDA

Bella!

ARNOLD

Wanda, wait! Be careful! Wanda!

[WANDA falls off the branch, pulling ARNOLD with her. At the last second, he grabs onto a twig, stopping them from falling. They hang there. ARNOLD dangles from the twig and WANDA holds onto ARNOLD'S foot.]

ARNOLD

What do we do now, Wanda?

[They look down— see cat looking up hungrily—look at each other . . .]

WANDA AND ARNOLD

Heeeeellllppp!!!

[SFX: CREAKING BRANCH AS A CREATURE JUMPS OFF.]

[WIDEN to include the hopping creature that caught CAT's eye. It lands in front of CAT down below. It's a praying mantis.]

ARNOLD

[through clenched teeth] That wasn't Bella, Wanda!

WANDA

So? I knew that!

ARNOLD

Then WHY ARE WE HERE??!?

[SFX: BEEP! BEEP! OF BUS/FROG.]

[SHOT OF BUS/FROG hopping onto a branch below ARNOLD and WANDA. Its roof opens and a large funnel emerges. A cheerful and relaxed MS. FRIZZLE is at the wheel and calls through a bullhorn.]

MS. FRIZZLE

Wanda? Arnold? Come along now! I can't have you two hanging out here all day!

[ARNOLD and WANDA let go and BUS/FROG catches them. BUS/FROG closes its "eyes," leaps off the branch, lands on the ground, and hops away.]

RALPHIE

Here we go again!

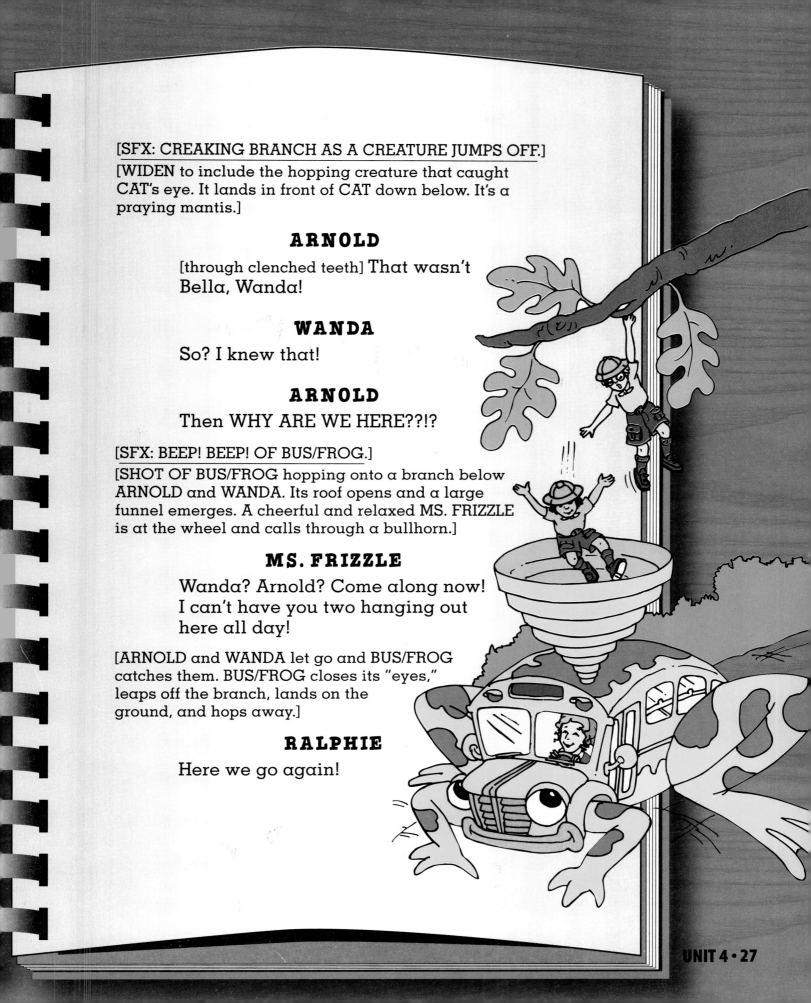

FROM THE DESK OF MS. FRIZZLE

We followed Bella's trail to a quiet pond and found her sitting on a lily pad. Wanda realized that the pond was a perfect home for Bella, so she tearfully said goodbye. Back in our classroom, Wanda had a real case of the bullfrog blues. But Wanda's sad tale has a "hoppy" ending. We made Wanda a giant paper frog to cheer her up. And that frog's habitat is the classroom.

THE END

THE VOICES BEHIND THE SCENES

MALCOLM-JAMAL WARNER

If the Producer, who often appears at the end of each episode, sounds familiar, it's no wonder! You're hearing the voice of **Malcolm-Jamal Warner.** The actor played Theo on the popular TV comedy, *The Cosby Show*.

LILY TOMLIN

Actress **Lily Tomlin** was perfect for the voice of Ms. Frizzle. After experimenting with many different voices, Tomlin found one that seemed just right—chirpy and cheerful! She won an Emmy for her portrayal.

LITTLE RICHARD

Famous rock 'n' roll star **Little Richard** sings *The Magic School Bus* theme song. His hits include a rock 'n' roll version of "Itsy Bitsy Spider."

LISA YAMANAKA

The voice of Wanda is recorded by **Lisa Yamanaka**. She can also be heard in two other animated TV series, *Little Rosey* and *Family Dog*.

Joanna Cole & Bruce Degen

Author and Illustrator

Creating *books is more fun than* **riding a** roller coaster!

Who really drives the Magic School Bus? Did you say Ms. Frizzle? Well, think again. The brains behind the wheel are Joanna Cole and Bruce Degen. Together they create this exciting series.

PROFILE

Names: Joanna Cole, Bruce Degen

Job:
Cole: author
Degen: illustrator

Former jobs:
Cole: baby-sitter, TV factory worker, editor
Degen: opera-scenery painter, art teacher

Favorite school subjects:
Cole: science
Degen: art and reading

First published books:
Cole: Cockroaches
Degen: Aunt Possum and the Pumpkin Man

Where you'd like to go on the Magic School Bus:
Cole: inside the human body
Degen: the South Seas

QUESTIONS

for Joanna Cole and Bruce Degen, Author and Illustrator

Here's how *author* Joanna Cole and *illustrator* Bruce Degen create a *hit series.*

Q How did The Magic School Bus books come about?

A *Cole:* I had been writing children's science books for about 15 years when I began the Magic School Bus series. The idea was a teacher who loves science would take her class on trips where no kids had ever gone before.

Q How do you decide what to write about?

A *Degen:* We brainstorm together. Once, on a cross-country plane trip, we came up with a list of 40 possible topics for our books!

Q What's it like working together on a series?

A *Cole:* Bruce and I make a good team! I research and write the book.
Degen: Then I come up with illustrations that go with the text. We have many meetings to figure out exactly what words and pictures go on every page.

Q **Was Ms. Frizzle inspired by a real person?**

A *Cole:* Oh, yes. I had a science teacher who was just like Ms. Frizzle—she was so enthusiastic about science! Ms. Frizzle is also a lot like me. I like to explain science to kids.

Q **How did you decide what to make Ms. Frizzle look like?**

A *Degen:* I pictured my high school teachers, who often wore simple dresses. To make Ms. Frizzle look distinctive, I added outrageous patterns.

Q **What about Arnold?**

A *Cole:* Arnold likes to stay at home—he's the opposite of Ms. Frizzle!

Q **What's the best thing about working on this series?**

A *Degen:* It's exciting!
Cole: We're always learning something new.

Joanna Cole and Bruce Degen's
Tips to Young Writers

1 Think of an interesting topic or story. Research it.

2 Plan what you're going to write. Make sketches.

3 Put the text and art together to make a book.

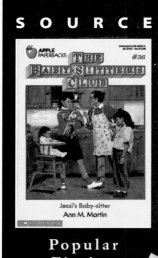

**Popular
Fiction**

AWARD
WINNING

Authors

from

THE BABY·SITTERS CLUB

Jessi's Baby-sitter

by **Ann M. Martin**

illustrated by Scott Ernster

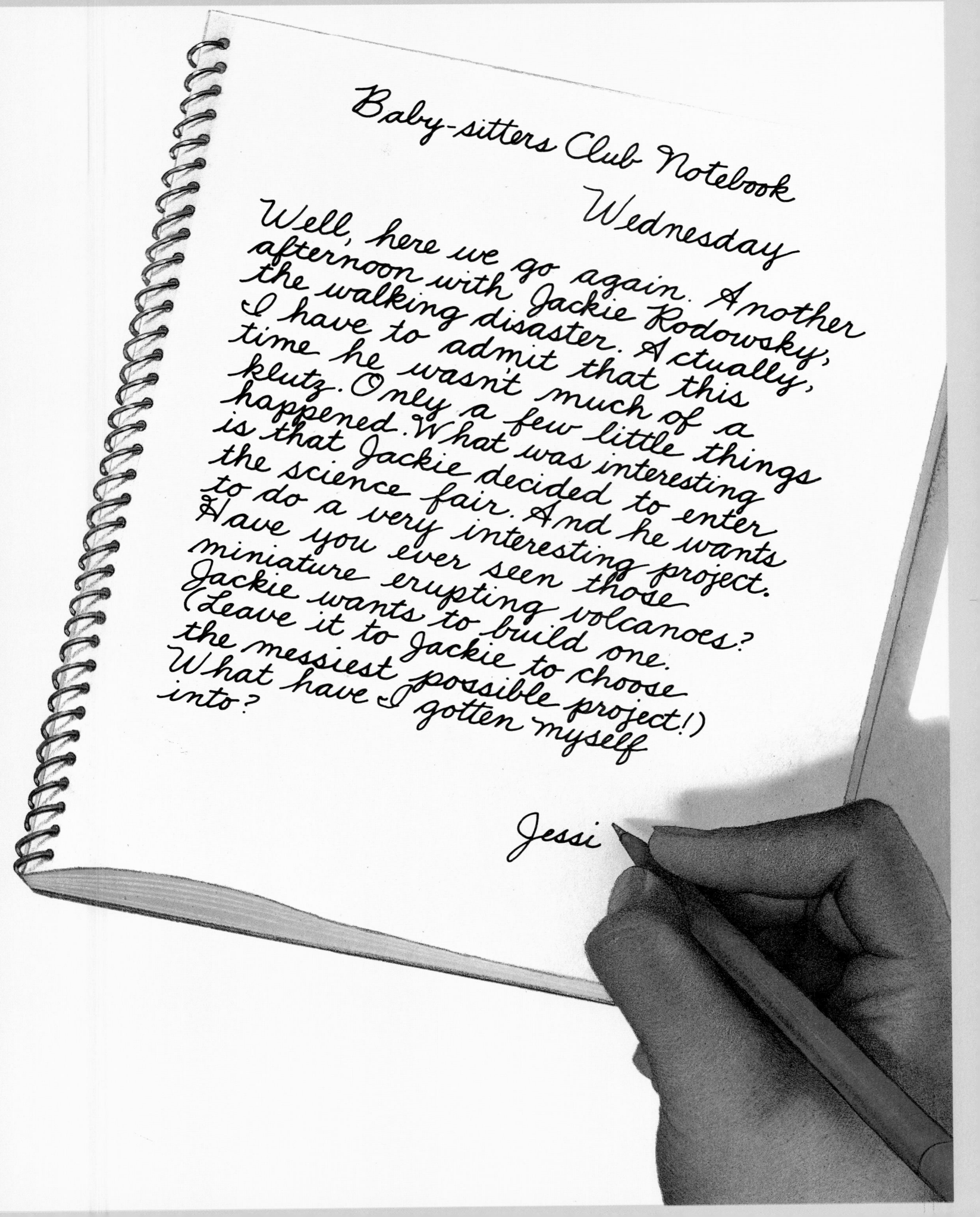

Baby-sitters Club Notebook

Wednesday

Well, here we go again. Another afternoon with Jackie Rodowsky, the walking disaster. Actually, I have to admit that this time he wasn't much of a klutz. Only a few little things happened. What was interesting is that Jackie decided to enter the science fair. And he wants to do a very interesting project. Have you ever seen those miniature erupting volcanoes? Jackie wants to build one. (Leave it to Jackie to choose the messiest possible project!) What have I gotten myself into?

Jessi

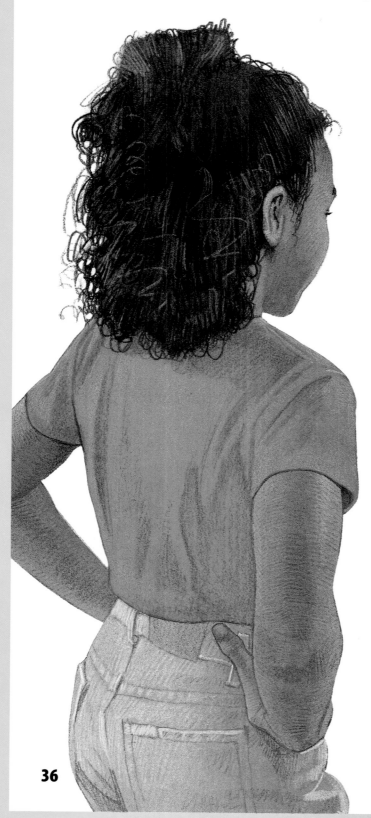

It was the evening of the science fair. I was so excited, you'd think *I'd* entered a project in it. (Well, in a way I had.) Anyway, the kids who were entering had to arrive at Stoneybrook Elementary by six-thirty in order to set up. The fair itself began at seven-thirty.

So at six-thirty, there were Stacey and Charlotte, Mal and Margo, Kristy and David Michael, Jackie and me, and a whole lot of kids and their parents or brothers or sisters or grandparents. Actually, Jackie and I had arrived at 6:20 to make sure we got our table staked out.

Now, at nearly seven o'clock, the all-purpose room was noisy and busy. All around Jackie and me were sighs of relief (when things went right) and groans (when things went wrong). Kids walked by carrying everything from huge pumpkins to complicated electrical things. I could hear the sounds of gears turning, tools tinkering, and video equipment. The all-purpose room was a pretty exciting place to be in.

"How do you feel, Jackie?" I asked him.

His volcano was loaded up and ready to explode. The "Welcome to the World of Volcanic Activity" sign was hung. His pointer was in his hand.

"Fine," he replied, but he sounded nervous. "Listen to this: Igneous rocks are born from fire, the molting—"

"Molten," I corrected him.

"The molten rock that lies several feet—"

"Miles."

"Okay. Several miles below the surface of our wonderful earth."

"Just *our earth*, Jackie. Don't overdo it."

Jackie nodded miserably.

Seven-thirty. The all-purpose room had really filled up. Teachers and parents and families and friends were pouring in.

"Look!" cried Jackie. "There are Mom and Dad and Archie and Shea!"

Boy, did Jackie seem relieved.

The Rodowskys made a beeline for The World of Volcanic Activity.

"Your project looks great, son," exclaimed Jackie's father.

WeLcome to the woRLD of VoLcanic Activity

"Yeah, it really does," Shea managed to admit.

"You know what?" I said. "I think I'm going to look around at the other projects before the judging begins. Jackie, you stay here and answer questions—but don't set the volcano off, okay?"

Jackie laughed. "Okay." He was beginning to feel pleased with himself. Even Shea hadn't seen the volcano explode. Jackie couldn't wait for the big moment. He wanted to prove something to Shea who, as his big brother, was always several steps ahead of him.

I walked slowly around the room, looking at the displays and experiments. I saw a model of a human heart made from Play-Doh (I think). I saw a small-scale "dinosaur war." I saw an impressive project about the Ice Age. I saw Charlotte's plants with her charts and graphs. One plant was considerably more healthy-looking than the other two, which were sort of scraggly.

"Which plant is that?" I asked, pointing to the full, green one.

"Guess," she said.

"The one that listened to classical music."

"Wrong." Charlotte grinned. "It's the Duran Duran plant. I'm not sure why. Maybe they were just really *fresh* seeds."

I laughed, and continued my walk through the exhibits. When I got back to Jackie's display, I found his family preparing to take a look around, so I said I'd stay with Jackie.

The volcano attracted a lot of attention.

"Neat! What's that?" asked a curly-headed boy.

"A volcano," said Jackie proudly. "It can *erupt*. It makes ash and lava go everywhere. It's really messy."

"Can I see?" asked the boy.

Jackie's face fell. "Sorry. I can only make it explode once. I have to wait until the judges are here. You can see it then."

"Okay," said the boy, looking disappointed.

A few seconds later two girls walked by.

"A volcano!" exclaimed one. "Hey, I've always wondered. What *does* make a volcano?"

Jackie was prepared. "Igneous rocks are born from fire…" He said the entire speech without one mistake. I gave him the thumbs-up sign.

The girl frowned. "But *why*," she went on, "do igneous rocks do that? I mean, why does heat make a volcano erupt?"

Jackie was stumped. That wasn't part of his speech. And he couldn't demonstrate the volcano to the girls, either.

Just when I was beginning to feel bad, my own family showed up. Well, Mama and Daddy and Becca did. Squirt was at home with Aunt Cecilia. Becca had come because she wanted to see Charlotte's experiment, and my parents were there because of the volcano they'd been hearing about.

I began to feel better.

At eight o'clock, an announcement came over the PA system.

"Attention, please. May I have your attention? The judging will now begin. All participants in the science fair prepare to demonstrate and explain your projects to the judges. Visitors, please stand at the back of the room during the judging."

"That was our *prin*cipal," Jackie informed me.

(You'd have thought the President of the United States had just spoken.)

"Good luck, Jackie," I said. "I know you'll do fine. When it's time to make the volcano erupt, tell the judges you have to call me to light the match because you're not allowed to do that yourself."

Jackie swallowed and nodded. I joined my family at the back of the room.

The judging began.

Two women and a man walked solemnly from table to table. They looked each project over. They requested demonstrations. They asked questions.

welcome to the world of volcanic Activity

Asked questions? Oh, no! Jackie couldn't talk about anything that wasn't in his speech. I hoped fervently that the judges would be so impressed with his demonstration that they wouldn't ask him any questions.

Tick, tick, tick. It was almost eight-thirty.

At last the judges reached The World of Volcanic Activity. I saw Jackie whisper something to one of the women. Then he saw me in the crowd and motioned for me to come forward. I did so, matches in hand.

"This," said Jackie as I reached his table, "is Jessi. She's my helper. She has to light the match for me."

(The judges smiled.)

I lit the match, told everyone to stand back, and tossed the match in the volcano. Jackie threw his hands in the air and cried, "The miracle of a volcano comes to life before our very eyes!"

PHOO! Lava was everywhere! It almost spattered the judges. Then it settled into a nice gooey flow down the sides of the volcano. The judges looked extremely impressed.

I stood to the side as Jackie made his speech, using the pointer.

The judges nodded and smiled. And then the questions began.

"How," asked the man, "is the crater of a volcano created?"

"Um," said Jackie. He looked at me, but I couldn't help him. "Um," he said again. "I don't know." At least he didn't admit that I'd practically done the project for him.

"Well … what happens to the lava when it has flowed out of the crater?" asked one of the women.

"It—it's very hot…" Jackie said lamely.

I looked at the ground. This was my fault. I felt terrible as I watched the judges make notations on their pads of paper. They walked on to the last project of the fair without even telling Jackie, "Good work," or "Nice going."

I went back to my parents and waited guiltily and nervously for the results of the fair to be announced.

"Jackie's project was great!" Dad said to me. "I've never seen such a thing. You really helped him."

A little too much, I thought.

Several minutes later, another announcement crackled over the loudspeaker. "The judges," said the principal, "have reached their decisions." (The judges were standing in the center of the room.) "They have chosen first-, second-, and third-place winners. When the winners are announced, will they please receive their ribbons from the judges? Thank you." There was a pause. Then the principal continued. "Third prize goes to Charlotte Johanssen for her project entitled 'The Power of Music.'"

Applause broke out. Charlotte, looking shy but pleased, edged over to the judges, received her yellow ribbon, and scurried back to her table, where she proudly attached the ribbon to the sign she'd made for her project.

The next two winners were announced. They went to kids I didn't know. I sought out Kristy, Mal, and my other friends in the crowd. Except for Stacey, they looked as disappointed as I felt.

But nobody looked more disappointed than Jackie, even though an Honorable Mention ribbon was already being fastened to his desk. (Every kid except the three winners was given an Honorable Mention.) The Rodowskys and I crowded around The World of Volcanic Activity.

"Don't be too upset, honey," Mrs. Rodowsky told Jackie.

I had to speak up. "He has a right to be upset," I said.

Mr. and Mrs. Rodowsky turned to me. "Why?" they asked at the same time.

"Because—because I gave him so much help with his project that he really didn't do much of it himself."

"Yeah," said Jackie, giving me the evil eyeball.

"I'm really sorry," I went on. "I just wanted him to win. He's always saying he's no good at anything, or that he has bad luck. I wanted him to see that he *can* be a winner. I guess I went about it all wrong, though."

Mr. and Mrs. Rodowsky were really nice. They understood what had happened. I got the feeling that they might have done things like this for Jackie in the past. Mr. Rodowsky even admitted to building the glass and wood box for the volcano himself. (Well, with a *teeny* bit of help from Jackie.)

But Jackie, who's usually so easygoing and sunny, continued to scowl at me. "I just wanted to have fun," he said. "That was all. I just wanted to make a volcano erupt."

"Jackie, Jessi apologized to you," his father said gently.

"I know." Jackie finally managed a smile. But it quickly turned to a frown. "Oh, no," he muttered. "Here come John, Ian, and Danny. They're going to laugh at me. I just know it."

But the three boys who approached us looked excited.

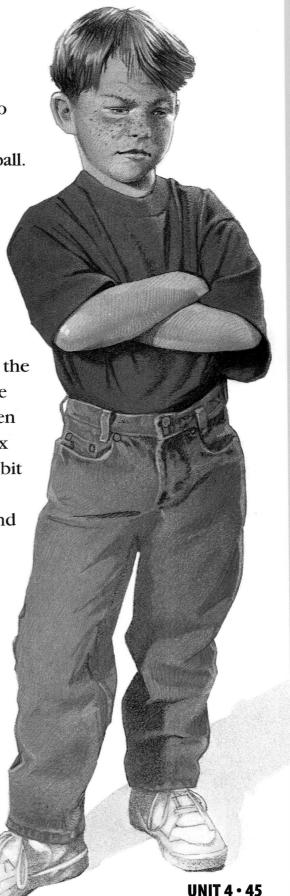

"Jackie," said one, "your volcano was totally rad. Make it explode again!"

"Yeah," said another. "That was so cool."

Jackie explained why he couldn't "explode" the volcano again.

"Oh, well," said the boys. "It was still awesome."

They started to walk away. "See you in school on Monday!" one called over his shoulder.

Jackie grinned at me like the Cheshire Cat. "I don't believe it!" he cried.

Mr. and Mrs. Rodowsky were smiling, too. "You know," said Jackie's mom, "there'll be another science fair next year. Jessi, maybe you could try helping Jackie again."

"I don't think so," I said. "I better not."

"Good," replied Jackie. "Because if I'm going to lose, I want to do it all by myself!"

How to
Make a Character Fact File

the series in which the character appears ●·········

the character's name ●·········

age ●·········

what the character looks like ●·········

Authors of hit series have fantastic imaginations! They create characters that appear in books, TV series, comics, or even video games. How do series authors keep track of the characters they create? One way is to make a fact file for each character.

What is a character fact file? A character fact file tells important details about a character.

SERIES:
The Baby-sitters Club

CHARACTER:
Jackie Rodowsky

- seven years old
- red hair, red cheeks, freckles
- big grin, with one tooth missing
- has two brothers, Shea and Archie
- loses tooth playing ball; likes losing teeth
- hits a home run and breaks the window of his elementary school
- baby-sitter, Jessi, helps him make a working volcano for the science fair; but she does most of the work
- is called the "walking disaster"
- is accident-prone
- plays the kazoo in a band that the Baby-sitters Club organizes
- has a pet grasshopper named Elizabeth

facts about
the
character's
family

important
events in the
character's
life

other details about
the character

1 Create a Character

Think of a hit series you like. Then make up a new character who can appear in the series. You might create a new superhero, a girl detective who helps Encyclopedia Brown, a new neighbor for Charlie Brown, a cat who helps Lassie, or a new friend for Ramona Quimby. There are hundreds of series in need of new characters.

TOOLS

• pencil and paper

• colored pencils or marking pens

Tips
• A character can be like someone you know.
• A character can have special talents—jumping rope, leaping tall buildings, or being a computer whiz.
• A character can do unusual things—a pig who can fly, or a boy who can see in the dark.

2 List Character Facts

What is your character like? These questions can help you think of details about your character. Jot down your ideas.

- In which series will this character appear?
- What is the character's name?
- What does the character look like?
- Where does the character live?
- What hobbies does the character have?
- Is the character funny, serious, friendly, helpful, or playful?

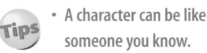

Angela the Detective

Roberto The Robot

3 Make a Fact File

Now you can make a character fact file. At the top of a sheet of paper, write the character's name. Below the name, write all the information you have made up about the character. Be sure to include the series in which the character will appear. If you wish, draw a picture of your character on a separate sheet of paper. Put it with the character's fact file.

4 Discuss Your Character

You have written down a lot of information about the character you created. Now let your classmates read your character fact file. Answer questions about the character. Compare the character to the ones your classmates have created. Will any of the characters appear in the same series?

If You Are Using a Computer ...

You can use your Journal format to write about your character on your computer, too. Use clip art to show what your character looks like.

THINK

Writers often put bits of themselves into characters. How is the character that you just created similar to or different from the real you?

Joanna Cole and
Bruce Degen
Author and Illustrator ▶

A Series for Everyone

Get the facts about insects from a series that features fabulous photos.

Figure out some picture riddles. Then learn how the eye-catching photographic clues are created.

Join a famous boy detective as he solves a mystery. Track down a cartoon criminal who's a hit in a computer game and on TV.

WORKSHOP 2

Review your favorite hit series.

CREATIVE EXPRESSION

ANTWON BUTLER
age 8

LITTLE HOUSE IN THE BIG WOODS

53

from # Incredible

Hard cases

There are more kinds of beetles than any other animal in the world. We know of about 300,000 species so far, compared to only 4,500 species of mammals.

Ladybug

Tiny giraffe

The giraffe weevil is a type of beetle with a very long neck. Nobody knows why it is this shape.

A neck twice as long as its body

Giraffe weevil

Beetles have tough wing cases that shield most of their bodies.

Mini-Beasts

by
Christopher Maynard

Spot the spots

The ladybug is a bright red beetle speckled with black spots. These spots warn birds that ladybugs taste absolutely awful.

Powerful jaws for biting and chewing

Mouth on a pole

Many weevils' jaws are on the end of a long snout. This makes it easy for them to drill holes through wood and nuts.

Frog beetle

Grabbing a bite to eat

Frog march

Frog beetles have strong back legs that they use to leap away from danger—just like frogs. Once clear, they unfold their hind wings and fly away to safety.

Beetles use their hind legs to take off.

Munching machines

Caterpillars are eating machines.
A single one can polish off every leaf on
a bush during just a few days of nonstop
feasting.

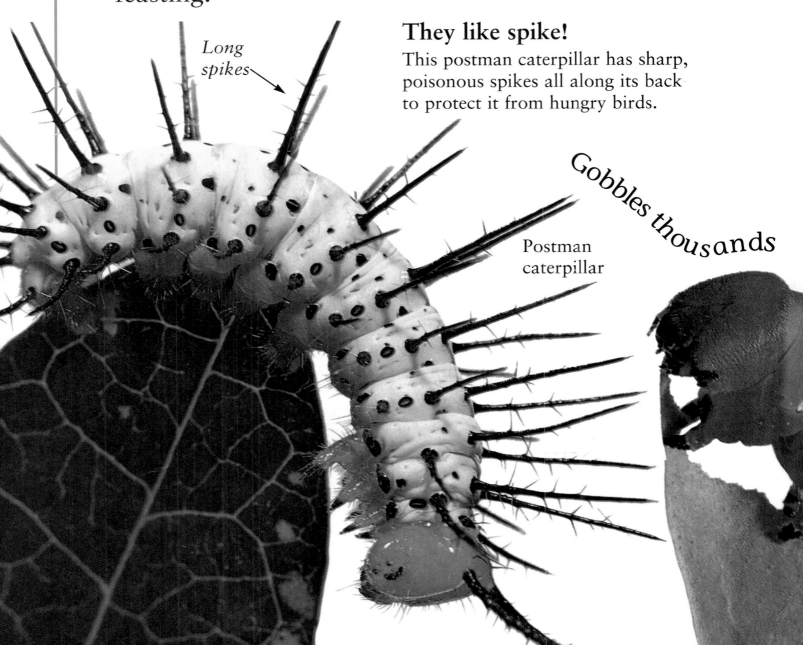

Long spikes

They like spike!
This postman caterpillar has sharp,
poisonous spikes all along its back
to protect it from hungry birds.

Gobbles thousands

Postman
caterpillar

*Eats poisonous leaves
to become poisonous itself*

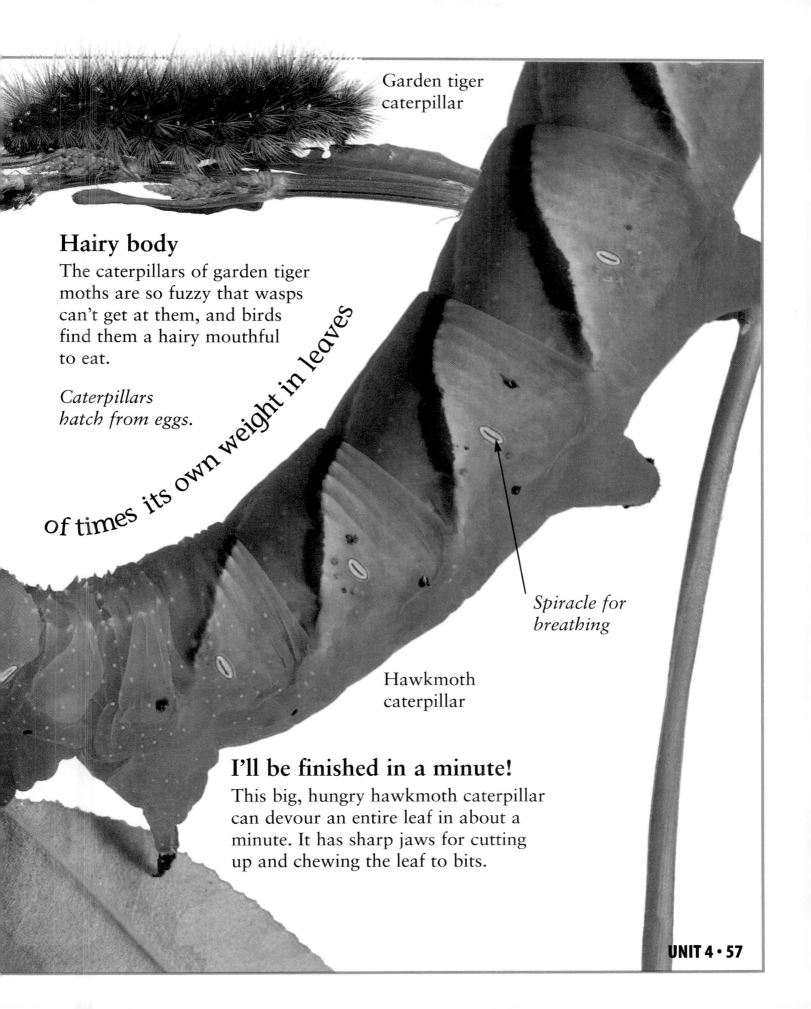

Garden tiger caterpillar

Hairy body

The caterpillars of garden tiger moths are so fuzzy that wasps can't get at them, and birds find them a hairy mouthful to eat.

Caterpillars hatch from eggs.

of times its own weight in leaves

Spiracle for breathing

Hawkmoth caterpillar

I'll be finished in a minute!

This big, hungry hawkmoth caterpillar can devour an entire leaf in about a minute. It has sharp jaws for cutting up and chewing the leaf to bits.

Handy legs

Grasshoppers and crickets have long hind legs and strong thigh muscles that are perfect for taking terrific leaps and bounds.

Cricket

King of the spring!
A cricket folds its long legs back, then springs upward.

Hind legs

Camouflaged as leaves and bark

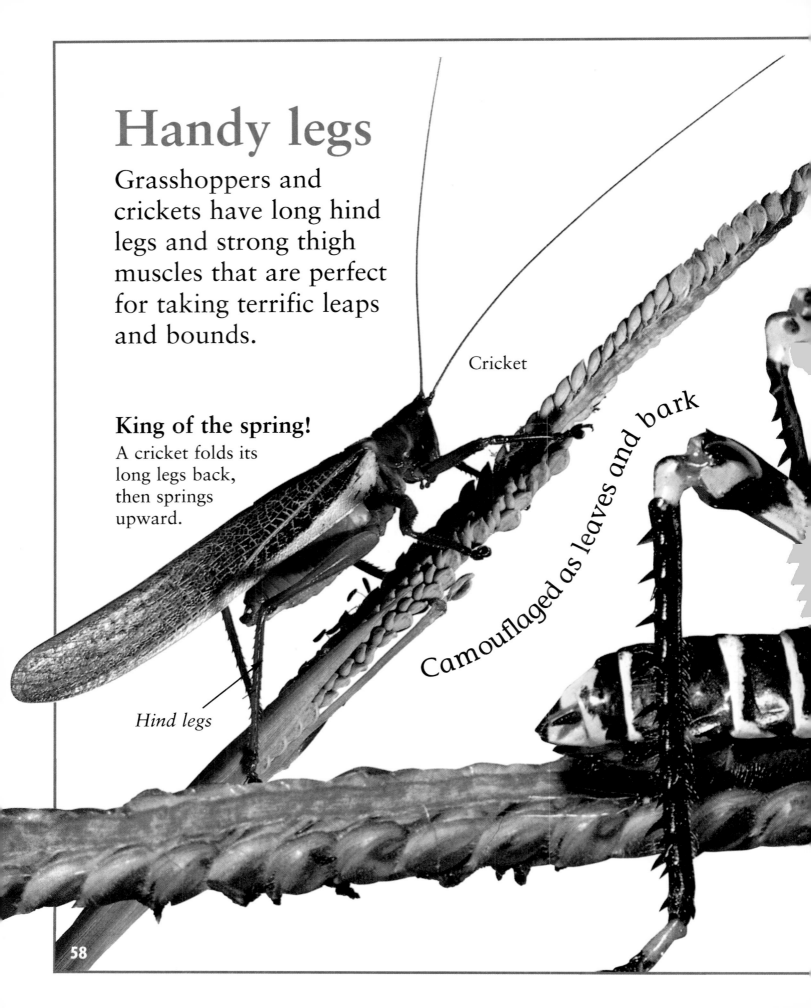

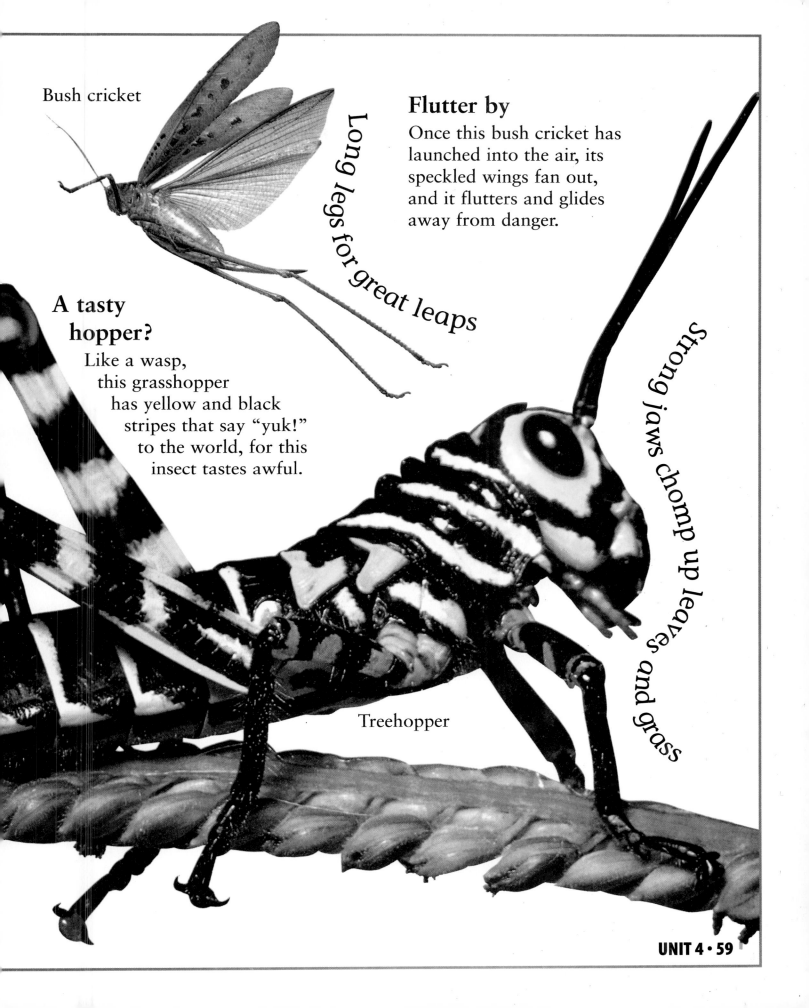

Bush cricket

Long legs for great leaps

Flutter by

Once this bush cricket has launched into the air, its speckled wings fan out, and it flutters and glides away from danger.

A tasty hopper?

Like a wasp, this grasshopper has yellow and black stripes that say "yuk!" to the world, for this insect tastes awful.

Strong jaws chomp up leaves and grass

Treehopper

Seriously deadly

A hairy tarantula may be scary to look at, but watch out for its bite! It is deadly to birds and small animals, but only as bad as a bee sting to human beings.

Look out for a spider that's big and hairy!

Tarantula

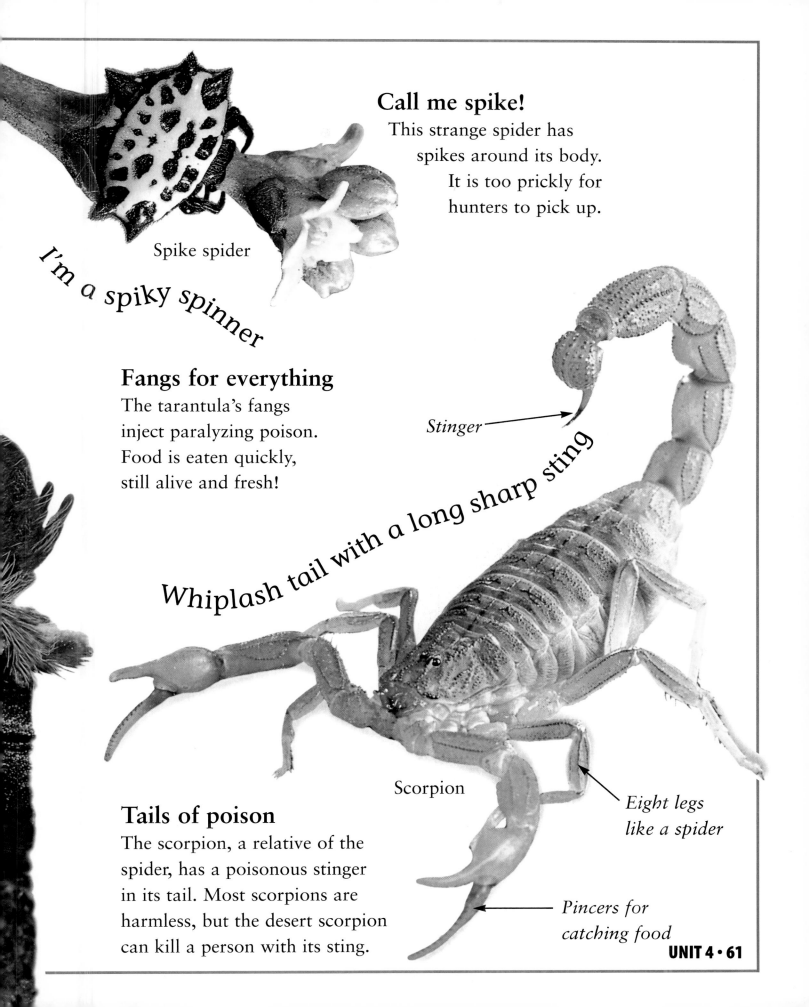

Call me spike!
This strange spider has spikes around its body. It is too prickly for hunters to pick up.

Spike spider

I'm a spiky spinner

Fangs for everything
The tarantula's fangs inject paralyzing poison. Food is eaten quickly, still alive and fresh!

Stinger

Whiplash tail with a long sharp sting

Tails of poison
The scorpion, a relative of the spider, has a poisonous stinger in its tail. Most scorpions are harmless, but the desert scorpion can kill a person with its sting.

Scorpion

Eight legs like a spider

Pincers for catching food

from

I SPY

Photographs by Walter Wick
Riddles by Jean Marzollo

AWARD
WINNING

Books

I spy a shovel, a long silver chain,
A little toy horse, a track for a train;

A birthday candle, a pretty gold ring,
A small puzzle piece, and a crown for a king.

I spy a turtle, a penny for a wish,

A door ajar, and a jewelry fish;

Four anchors, a ship, a shadowy whale,
A pot of gold, and A MERMAID'S TALE.

THE MAKING OF I SPY

It takes a quick mind and a sharp eye,
To bring you the series that's known as I SPY!

Jean Marzollo and Walter Wick put their talents together in the eye-catching I SPY series.

Getting Started

Each book begins with Jean Marzollo and Walter Wick discussing a theme and brainstorming ideas for the photos. Then Wick goes looking for objects for the photographs.

The number of items needed for each photo is mind-boggling! Wick's search takes him to flea markets, crafts shops, toy stores, and even friends' attics.

Wick sets up the shot.

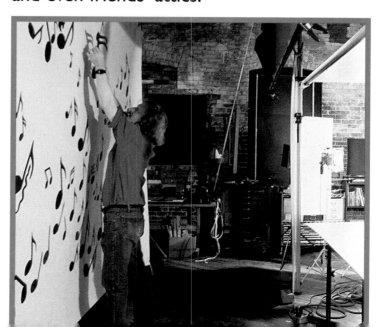

Everything is in place.

Shooting *I SPY*

To create one of the photographs for *I SPY Fun House*, Wick first built a wooden frame. From it he hung shiny musical instruments. Next he glued cut-out musical notes onto a white wall. Special lights made the wall look blue.

Wick placed colorful toy clowns above the instruments so they would be reflected in the horns. It took several days for everything to look just right. When it did, Wick shot the picture. Lights! Camera! Click!

This is "Circus Band," one of the photos that appeared in *I SPY Fun House.*

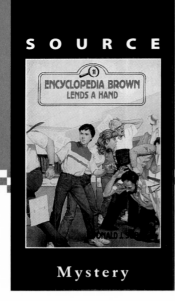

from
ENCYCLOPEDIA BROWN
LENDS A HAND

THE CASE of the

RUNAWAY ELEPHANT

by **Donald J. Sobol**

illustrated by Leonard Shortall

Across the length and breadth of America people were wondering:

"What is Idaville's secret?"

For more than a year now, no one had gotten away with a crime in Idaville.

Aside from being a model of law and order, Idaville was a lovely seaside town. It had clean beaches and three movie theaters. It had churches, a synagogue, four banks, and two delicatessens.

The chief of police was Mr. Brown. He knew that nearly every American thought he was the best peace officer in the nation. He also knew the truth about Idaville.

The real brains behind Idaville's war on crime was his only child, ten-year-old Encyclopedia.

Whenever Chief Brown had a mystery he could not solve, he put his emergency plan into action. He went home to dinner. At the table he told Encyclopedia the facts.

The boy detective solved the case before dessert. Once in a while, however, he had to ask for second helpings to gain more time.

Chief Brown hated keeping his son's ability a secret. He felt Congress should award Encyclopedia a vote of thanks. But how could he suggest it?

Who would believe that the guiding hand behind Idaville's police record could make a yo-yo loop-the-loop off a man-on-the-flying trapeze?

"Mr. Hunt opened his eyes, and there was Jimbo peeping
through the window."

No one.

So Chief Brown said nothing.

Encyclopedia never let slip a word about the help he gave his father. He did not want to seem different from other fifth-graders.

But he was stuck with his nickname.

Only his parents and teachers called him by his right name, Leroy. Everyone else in Idaville called him Encyclopedia.

An encyclopedia is a book or set of books filled with facts from A to Z. Encyclopedia had read so many books he was really more like a library. You might say he was the only library in which the information desk was on the top floor.

One evening Chief Brown looked up from his soup. "Friday the thirteenth," he muttered.

"You're mistaken, dear," said Mrs. Brown. "Today is Friday the twelfth."

"I'm talking about seventeen years ago," said Chief Brown.

"Does the date have something to do with a case?" asked Encyclopedia.

"Yes, with Mr. Hunt's elephant, Jimbo," answered Chief Brown. "The animal is causing a problem."

Encyclopedia refused to believe his ears. Jimbo was the only pet elephant in Idaville. He never caused anyone a problem. Mr. Hunt kept him in the backyard.

"If Jimbo is in the middle of a mystery, tell Leroy," urged Mrs. Brown. "It could be his biggest case."

Chief Brown nodded. "It turns out that Jimbo may not belong to Mr. Hunt after all," he began. "Mr. Hunt found him outside his bedroom window on April Fools' Day seventeen years ago."

"What a shock for him!" exclaimed Mrs. Brown.

"I imagine so," replied Chief Brown. "Mr. Hunt opened his eyes, and there was Jimbo peeping through the window. He woke up Mrs. Hunt to make sure he wasn't dreaming."

"What did she say?" asked Encyclopedia.

"'I hope he's on a leash,'" replied Chief Brown, "according to Mr. Hunt."

"Mr. Hunt has a great memory," marveled Encyclopedia.

"So does Mr. Xippas," said Chief Brown. "He came to my office today. He says he owns the elephant and wants him back. He claims Mr. Hunt never paid for Jimbo."

"What does Mr. Hunt say?" inquired Mrs. Brown.

"Mr. Hunt insists that he mailed the money to Mr. Xippas," said Chief Brown.

He waited while Mrs. Brown cleared the soup bowls. When she had served the ham loaf, he took his notebook from his breast pocket.

"I spoke with both Mr. Xippas and Mr. Hunt today," he said. "I'll give you Mr. Hunt's side first."

Encyclopedia and his mother listened as Chief Brown read from his notes.

"Mr. Hunt says that he thought the elephant in his backyard was a prank, since it was April Fools' Day. He immediately called the police. It turned out that the elephant had run away from a little circus which had just arrived in town.

"An hour later Mr. Xippas came to Mr. Hunt's house. Mr. Xippas owned and trained Jimbo. By then the Hunts had taken a liking to the animal. They asked Mr. Xippas if he would sell him.

"Mr. Xippas agreed. He also agreed to stay at the Hunts' house a week or two. The couple wanted to learn how to care for Jimbo. Mr. Xippas, however, asked to see their money first. So that afternoon Mr. Hunt drew the cash from the Oceanside Bank and showed it to the animal trainer.

"After nearly two weeks, the Hunts felt they could handle the friendly Jimbo. Mr. Hunt offered Mr. Xippas the money. Mr. Xippas wouldn't take it because it was Friday the thirteenth, which he said was bad luck for him.

"The same night Mr. Xippas left Idaville. He left a forwarding address, and Mr. Hunt mailed him the money."

Chief Brown looked up from his notebook.

"That's Mr. Hunt's story," he said. "Mr. Xippas insists he never got the money. The address was his sister's house in New Jersey. He says she was sick and had telephoned him to come and be with her."

"Why did Mr. Xippas wait seventeen years before coming back to Idaville to claim Jimbo?" asked Encyclopedia. "It doesn't sound right."

"He says his sister died shortly after he reached her bedside," replied Chief Brown. "A day after her death, he got an offer of a job in India. He's been overseas all this time. He only returned to the United States five days ago."

"I wonder about him," said Mrs. Brown. "Why did he ask to see Mr. Hunt's money that very first day? I don't think that was nice. He should have trusted Mr. Hunt."

"Mr. Xippas says he didn't ask to see the money," answered Chief Brown. "He says Mr. Hunt never went to the bank. Furthermore, the only reason he stayed so long with the Hunts was that every day Mr. Hunt promised to pay him the following day."

Chief Brown closed his notebook.

"I should add," he said, "that Mr. Xippas denies that he refused the money on Friday the thirteenth because it was bad luck. He says the only thing Mr. Hunt gave him were promises to pay."

"What about the bank?" said Mrs. Brown. "Don't banks keep records?"

"A hurricane struck later that year," said Chief Brown. "It flooded the Oceanside Bank, Mr. Hunt's home, and most of the buildings in Idaville. All the records were destroyed."

"I still don't understand something," said Mrs. Brown. "Mr. Xippas worked in the circus. How could he take nearly two weeks off to stay with the Hunts?"

"Mr. Xippas told me that he had become tired of circus life," said Chief Brown. "By selling Jimbo, he could quit and open his own business."

"Whom to believe?" sighed Mrs. Brown.

She had risen to clear the dishes and bring in the dessert. She glanced at Encyclopedia with concern. He always solved a case before dessert. Was this case too hard?

The boy detective closed his eyes. He always closed his eyes when he did his deepest thinking.

Suddenly his eyes opened. "Dad," he said. "Both men have memories like an elephant. But the one who is lying is Mr.———"

WHO?

Turn the page

for the **solution** *to* the case.

SOLUTION TO THE CASE of the RUNAWAY ELEPHANT

Mr. Hunt never paid for the elephant.

He lied when he said Mr. Xippas refused to accept payment on Friday the thirteenth because it was bad luck.

But what tripped him up was another lie. He said he had gone to the bank on April Fools' Day and had drawn out the money to buy Jimbo. Impossible!

Because it happened seventeen years ago, he thought he was safe. He had not reckoned on Encyclopedia.

April Fools' Day is April 1.

As Encyclopedia knew, if in any month a Friday falls on the thirteenth, the first day of the month is Sunday.

On Sundays banks are closed.

from

101 Elephant JokeS

Compiled by ROBERT BLAKE

Illustrated by PETER SPACEK

Why are **elephants** trumpeters?

It is too hard for them to learn to play the piano!

Why do elephants wear **blue** sneakers?

Their red ones are in the laundry!

Why do **elephants** wear sneakers while jumping from tree to tree?

They don't want to wake up the neighbors!

What time is it when an **elephant** sits on a fence?

Time to buy a new fence!

What's gray and white and red all over?

An embarrassed elephant!

Where do you find **elephants**?

It depends on where you leave them!

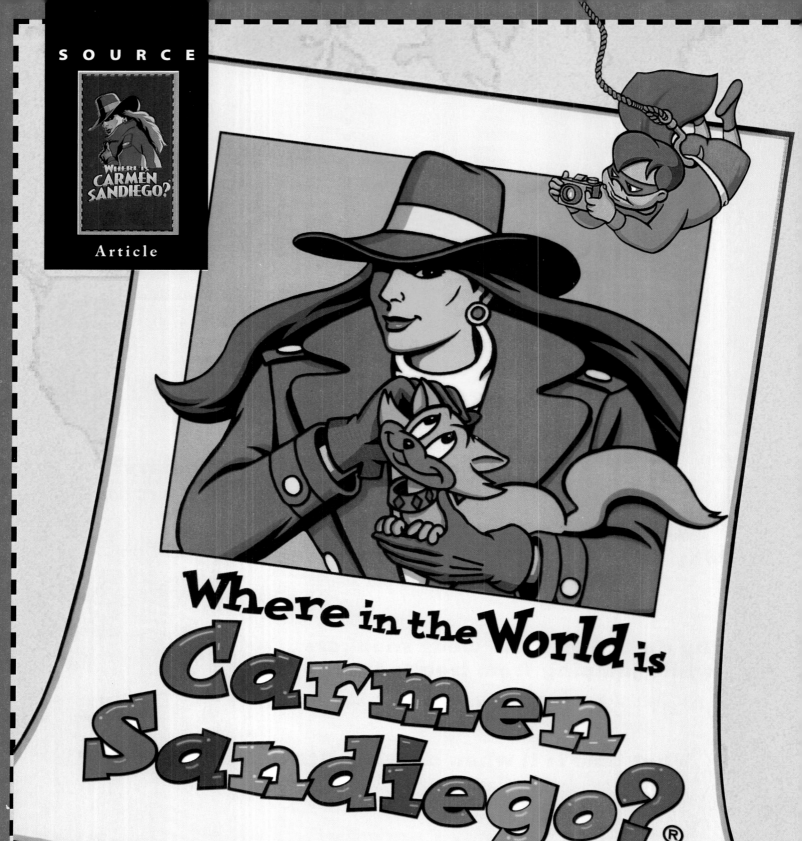

Where in the World is Carmen Sandiego?®

BY CHARLES NORDLANDER

WANTED:

CARMEN SANDIEGO

ACME Photo-Fax

Kids first chased Carmen on a black and white computer screen. Today they can track her in color.

All in the Game

Carmen Sandiego started her career in 1985 in the computer game called *Where in the World is Carmen Sandiego?*® Game players chased her all over the world. And sometimes, they even caught her!

Carmen Sandiego, in case you haven't heard, is the fictional leader of a bunch of thieves. Carmen and her crew nab famous buildings, monuments, and islands, too. Even the Empire State Building and the Grand Canyon aren't safe when Carmen is nearby.

Kids use their wits, knowledge of geography, and computer skills to catch the slippery leader.

A California company that makes computer software created Carmen Sandiego. The first game was such a big hit that many sequels followed. One version of the game even sends players into outer space to track her! And there's a Junior Detective Edition for gumshoes eight years old and younger.

Stretch the Crime Dog has a good nose for catching criminals.

TV Star

Carmen made her big jump to television in 1991 in the PBS series *Where in the World Is Carmen Sandiego?*® For the first time, kids without computers had a chance to catch her. At the same time, Carmen was making music news. Rockapella, the singing group who appears on the show, had people everywhere humming the Carmen Sandiego theme song.

As a TV star, Carmen Sandiego was not any easier to catch, but she certainly became easier to see. She began showing up every-where—in record stores, in books and magazines, and even on backpacks.

◀ Carmine the Cat is a purr-fect member of Carmen's team.

Carmen Sandiego recordings hit stores in 1992, with songs by the TV show's singing group, Rockapella.

Bad guys beware! Computer players get help from ACME Detective Agency crime-fighters Penelope Paparazzi and F-Stop Freddy.

On the TV show, guest detectives and host Greg Lee give Carmen a run for her money. Six million kids a week tune in to watch.

Charles Nordlander

is the head
scriptwriter for the
Carmen Sandiego
live-game show
on PBS. He has
written more than
245 episodes. Like
Carmen, he loves
to travel. Unlike
Carmen, he leaves
things where he
finds them!

A Real Page-Turner

Where do the facts on the
Carmen Sandiego TV show
come from? The folks at
National Geographic World, a
children's magazine, gather and
check all material used on the
show. But that's not all. The
editors at the magazine
decided it was time for
Carmen to appear in print. In
September 1992, Carmen
became a monthly comic strip
in their magazine.

The Future

What's next for Carmen?
Well, she has been spotted in
books, puzzles, a board game,
a calendar, and more. Soon
gumshoes may even be chasing
her across a movie screen!
One thing's for sure: Carmen
will have to get faster and
smarter to stay ahead of the
kids on her trail.

Hail to the Chief!

Lynne Thigpen plays the role of The Chief of Acme Crimenet on the PBS television show, *Where in the World Is Carmen Sandiego?* Here's what she has to say about the series:

"Why is *Carmen Sandiego* such a big hit with kids? First of all, it's fun. All kids like to have fun! But Carmen is more than that. The show gives kids credit for what they've *learned*. In fact, a lot of adults don't know the things that kids on *Carmen* know.

"A father told me about the birthday present his son wanted. He asked for large maps to hang by his bed. I was so thrilled that *Carmen Sandiego* could have that kind of effect!"

How to
Write a Series Review

author of
the series

How did you discover your favorite hit series? Did a friend tell you about it? Did you read a glowing review about it in a newspaper or magazine?

a favorite
scene

What is a review? A review is one person's opinion about a book, movie, cartoon, comic book, TV show, video game, or some other kind of entertainment.

how the
reviewer
feels about
the book

LITTLE HOUSE ON THE PRAIRIE • LAURA INGALLS WILDER

LITTLE HOUSE IN THE BIG WOODS • LAURA INGALLS WILDER

name of reviewer

ANTWON BUTLER
age 8

title of the review names one book in the series

where and when the story takes place

LITTLE HOUSE IN THE BIG WOODS

ILLUSTRATED BY GARTH WILLIAMS

Laura Ingalls Wilder is the author of *Little House in the Big Woods* and also its main character. This first book in the Little House series is about the Ingalls family, who lived in a cabin in northern Wisconsin a long time ago. I especially liked one chapter called "Dance at Grandpa's." Grandma dances and even beats Uncle George in a dance called a jig. I could picture that in my mind, and it made me laugh. The book also tells you how to make maple syrup.

When I finished reading this book, I was sad it was over. So I read the rest of the series. I think people should read these books because you find out that even though Laura lived many years ago she was still a kid, and kids will always have things in common.

R

1 Choose a Series

Choose a series to review. If you can't think of a series, ask a friend, teacher, or librarian to suggest a good one. Then gather several books, cartoons, or comics in the series. If you are reviewing a TV or movie series, jot down the titles of some episodes you have seen.

TOOLS

• pencil and paper

2 Make Notes

Make some notes about the series you have chosen. Here are some questions to help you:

* Is it a series you read or one that you watch?

* Is the series fiction or nonfiction? If it's fiction, what kind of story is it? If it's nonfiction, what topic does it tell about?

* What's the same in each book or episode? What's different?

* Who are your favorite characters? Why?

* Which book or episode do you want to review?

3 Write Your Review

Use your notes to write your review. Include the title of the episode, the series it came from, and the author. Tell what the series is about. Don't forget to describe an important scene from one episode. Be sure to tell your readers how you feel about the series. Last, but not least, sign your review, so everyone will know who wrote it.

4 Share Your Review

Read your review aloud to your classmates, and answer any questions they have. For anyone who is interested, you can suggest other favorite books or episodes in the series.

If You Are Using a Computer ...

Write your review in the Newsletter format. Create a headline. Use clip art so your review looks like a newspaper article.

Tip How do you rate the series you just reviewed? Was it fantastic, great, good, or just okay? Write your rating at the top of your review.

THINK

Reviewers tell their opinions about books, TV, movies, and music. Why do you think it's important to read these reviews?

Joanna Cole and Bruce Degen
Author and Illustrator ▶

Some series last for years and years.

Long-Running Hits

Meet adventure with the Ingalls family as they travel to a new "little house." Then explore a place where Laura once played.

Visit the old Southwest and discover a chile-flavored version of *The Three Little Pigs*.

PROJECT

Create an episode for a hit series.

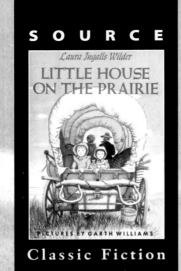

from

LITTLE HOUSE on the PRAIRIE

AWARD WINNING

Book

by Laura Ingalls Wilder
illustrated by Garth Williams

The Big Woods was getting too crowded. It was time to move West. So the Ingalls family—Pa, Ma, Mary, Laura, and baby Carrie—packed their belongings into a covered wagon and hitched up the horses, Pet and Patty. With Jack, their dog, trotting under the wagon, they began the long journey to a new home on the prairie.

Many miles later, the family was glad to see a good spot for camping among some trees ahead.

Pet and Patty began to trot briskly, as if they were glad, too. Laura held tight to the wagon bow and stood up in the jolting wagon. Beyond Pa's shoulder and far across the waves of green grass she could see the trees, and they were not like any trees she had seen before. They were no taller than bushes.

"Whoa!" said Pa, suddenly. "Now which way?" he muttered to himself.

The road divided here, and you could not tell which was the more-traveled way. Both of them were faint wheel tracks in the grass. One went toward the west, the other sloped downward a little, toward the south. Both soon vanished in the tall, blowing grass.

"Better go downhill, I guess," Pa decided. "The creek's down in the bottoms. Must be this is the way to the ford." He turned Pet and Patty toward the south.

The road went down and up and down and up again, over gently curving land. The trees were nearer now, but they were no taller. Then Laura gasped and clutched the wagon bow, for almost under Pet's and Patty's noses there was no more blowing grass, there was no land at all. She looked beyond the edge of the land and across the tops of trees.

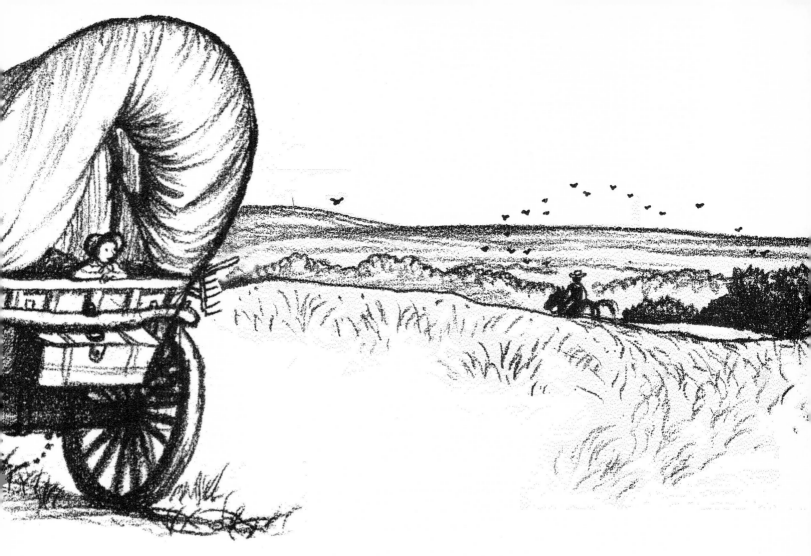

The road turned there. For a little way it went along the cliff's top, then it went sharply downward. Pa put on the brakes; Pet and Patty braced themselves backward and almost sat down. The wagon wheels slid onward, little by little lowering the wagon farther down the steep slope into the ground. Jagged cliffs of bare red earth rose up on both sides of the wagon. Grass waved along their tops, but nothing grew on their seamed, straight-up-and-down sides. They were hot, and heat came from them against Laura's face. The wind was still blowing overhead, but it did not blow into this deep crack in the ground. The stillness seemed strange and empty.

Then once more the wagon was level. The narrow
crack down which it had come opened into the
bottom lands. Here grew the tall trees whose tops
Laura had seen from the prairie above. Shady groves
were scattered on the rolling meadows, and in the
groves deer were lying down, hardly to be seen among
the shadows. The deer turned their heads toward
the wagon, and curious fawns stood up to see it
more clearly.

Laura was surprised because she did not see the
creek. But the bottom lands were wide. Down here,
below the prairie, there were gentle hills and open
sunny places. The air was still and hot. Under the
wagon wheels the ground was soft. In the sunny
open spaces the grass grew thin, and deer had
cropped it short.

For a while the high, bare cliffs of red earth stood up behind the wagon. But they were almost hidden behind hills and trees when Pet and Patty stopped to drink from the creek.

The rushing sound of the water filled the still air. All along the creek banks the trees hung over it and made it dark with shadows. In the middle it ran swiftly, sparkling silver and blue.

"This creek's pretty high," Pa said. "But I guess we can make it all right. You can see this is a ford, by the old wheel ruts. What do you say, Caroline?"

"Whatever you say, Charles," Ma answered.

Pet and Patty lifted their wet noses. They pricked their ears forward, looking at the creek; then they pricked them backward to hear what Pa would say. They sighed and laid their soft noses together to whisper to each other. A little way upstream, Jack was lapping the water with his red tongue.

STARTING OUT

Little House in the Big Woods was Laura Ingalls Wilder's first book in the series. She wrote it when she was 63 years old.

"I'll tie down the wagon-cover," Pa said. He climbed down from the seat, unrolled the canvas sides and tied them firmly to the wagon box. Then he pulled the rope at the back, so that the canvas puckered together in the middle, leaving only a tiny round hole, too small to see through.

Mary huddled down on the bed. She did not like fords; she was afraid of the rushing water. But Laura was excited; she liked the splashing. Pa climbed to the seat, saying, "They may have to swim, out there in the middle. But we'll make it all right, Caroline."

Laura thought of Jack and said, "I wish Jack could ride in the wagon, Pa."

Pa did not answer. He gathered the reins tightly in his hands. Ma said "Jack can swim, Laura. He will be all right."

The wagon went forward softly in mud. Water began to splash against the wheels. The splashing grew louder. The wagon shook as the noisy water struck at it. Then all at once the wagon lifted and balanced and swayed. It was a lovely feeling.

The noise stopped, and Ma said, sharply, "Lie down, girls!"

Quick as a flash, Mary and Laura dropped flat on the bed. When Ma spoke like that, they did as they were told. Ma's arm pulled a smothering blanket over them, heads and all.

"Be still, just as you are. Don't move!" she said.

Mary did not move; she was trembling and still.

But Laura could not help wriggling a little bit. She did so want to see what was happening. She could feel the wagon swaying and turning; the splashing was noisy again, and again it died away. Then Pa's voice frightened Laura. It said, "Take them, Caroline!"

The wagon lurched; there was a sudden heavy splash beside it. Laura sat straight up and clawed the blanket from her head.

Pa was gone. Ma sat alone, holding tight to the reins with both hands. Mary hid her face in the blanket again, but Laura rose up farther. She couldn't see the creek bank. She couldn't see anything in front of the wagon but water rushing at it. And in the water, three heads; Pet's head and Patty's head and Pa's small, wet head. Pa's fist in the water was holding tight to Pet's bridle.

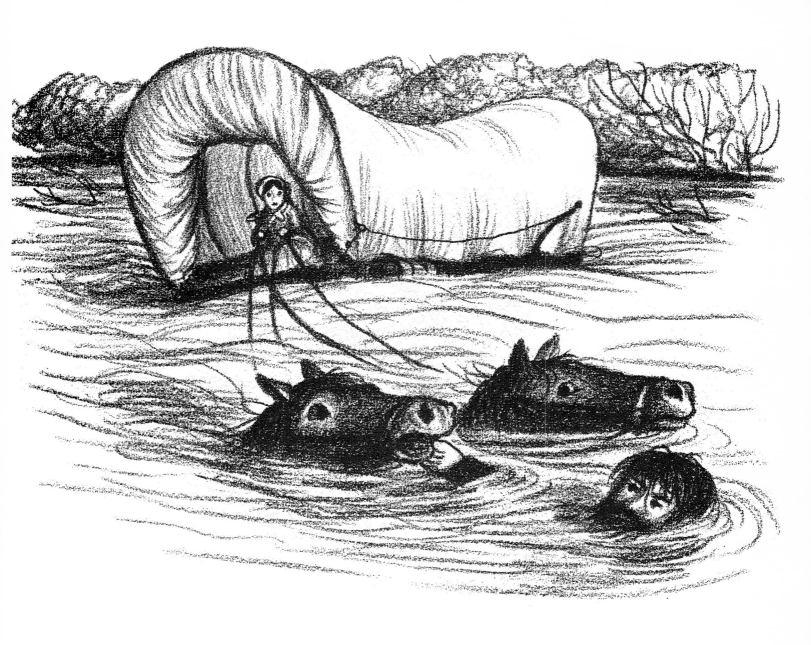

Laura could faintly hear Pa's voice through the
rushing of the water. It sounded calm and cheerful,
but she couldn't hear what he said. He was talking to
the horses. Ma's face was white and scared.

"Lie down, Laura," Ma said.

Laura lay down. She felt cold and sick. Her eyes
were shut tight, but she could still see the terrible
water and Pa's brown beard drowning in it.

For a long, long time the wagon swayed and swung, and Mary cried without making a sound, and Laura's stomach felt sicker and sicker. Then the front wheels struck and grated, and Pa shouted. The whole wagon jerked and jolted and tipped backward, but the wheels were turning on the ground. Laura was up again, holding to the seat; she saw Pet's and Patty's scrambling wet backs climbing a steep bank, and Pa running beside them, shouting, "Hi, Patty! Hi, Pet! Get up! Get up! Whoopsy-daisy! Good girls!"

At the top of the bank they stood still, panting and dripping. And the wagon stood still, safely out of that creek.

Pa stood panting and dripping, too, and Ma said, "Oh, Charles!"

"There, there, Caroline," said Pa. "We're all safe, thanks to a good tight wagon-box well fastened to the running-gear. I never saw a creek rise so fast in my life. Pet and Patty are good swimmers, but I guess they wouldn't have made it if I hadn't helped them."

ANOTHER HIT SERIES

The Little House books became a hit television series, too. Thousands of viewers began following the adventures of the Ingalls family in 1974.

If Pa had not known what to do, or if Ma had been too frightened to drive, or if Laura and Mary had been naughty and bothered her, then they would all have been lost. The river would have rolled them over and over and carried them away and drowned them, and nobody would ever have known what became of them. For weeks, perhaps, no other person would come along that road.

"Well," said Pa, "all's well that ends well," and Ma said, "Charles, you're wet to the skin."

Before Pa could answer, Laura cried, "Oh, where's Jack?"

They had forgotten Jack. They had left him on the other side of that dreadful water and now they could not see him anywhere. He must have tried to swim after them, but they could not see him struggling in the water now.

Laura swallowed hard, to keep from crying. She knew it was shameful to cry, but there was crying inside her. All the long way from Wisconsin poor Jack had followed them so patiently and faithfully, and now they had left him to drown. He was so tired, and they might have taken him into the wagon. He had stood on the bank and seen the wagon going away from him, as if they didn't care for him at all. And he would never know how much they wanted him.

Pa said he wouldn't have done such a thing to Jack, not for a million dollars. If he'd known how that creek would rise when they were in mid-stream, he would never have let Jack try to swim it. "But that can't be helped now," he said.

He went far up and down the creek bank, looking for Jack, calling him and whistling for him.

It was no use. Jack was gone.

Was Jack *really* swept away in the creek? Don't be kept in suspense! Read the rest of this exciting book to find out.

SEARCHING FOR LAURA INGALLS
A Reader's Journey

FROM

SEARCHING FOR LAURA INGALLS

A Reader's Journey

by Kathryn Lasky and Meribah Knight
photographs by Christopher G. Knight

Meribah Knight loved all of Laura Ingalls Wilder's *Little House* books. And she wanted to visit Laura's many homes more than anything. One summer Meribah's wish came true. She and her family traveled by camper to some of the places Laura Ingalls had lived, including Plum Creek in western Minnesota.

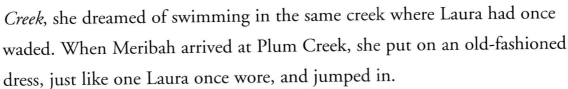

In 1873 the Ingalls family had moved from Wisconsin to a dugout house that was built near Plum Creek. Laura was only six, and she couldn't swim. But she loved to wade in the creek on hot summer days and cool her toes in the clear water.

After Meribah read *On the Banks of Plum Creek*, she dreamed of swimming in the same creek where Laura had once waded. When Meribah arrived at Plum Creek, she put on an old-fashioned dress, just like one Laura once wore, and jumped in.

Here is how Meribah described Plum Creek in her diary.

◄ Meribah finds that this covered wagon, like the one Laura rode in, is very different from travel in a modern camper (above).

I finally had my dream come true, but it was almost a bad dream, a nightmare. I got to go wading and swimming in Plum Creek. ▼

It was warm and the current in the creek was going really fast. When I waded into the water I fell, but I got used to it and started to swim. When I stood up my clothes were heavy and wet. I felt like stones were hanging on my skirt. I climbed trees that were sticking out over the creek. ▶

◄ I remembered in the book how Laura went to look under branches and rocks for the old crab, the one she used to scare Nellie Oleson, the stuck-up girl in the book. I looked for it, too. I couldn't find it, so I swam along some more and hung from branches.

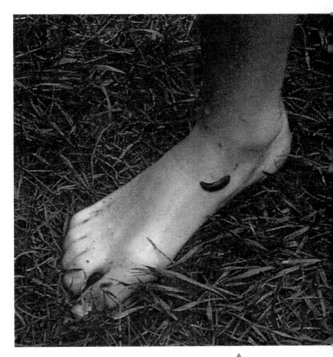

▲

But guess what? When I came out of Plum Creek I saw this thing that looked like a glob of mud on my foot, and then I thought, It's a black slug, but then I thought, Slugs aren't black. Then I remembered. It came back all awful. It was a leech just like the ones Laura got on her. I had forgotten this whole part of the book, the part about the leeches. My stomach flip-flopped, my brain went crazy, and I started to scream. Of course my dad just had to take a picture before he pulled it off me.

THE THREE LITTLE JAVELINAS

by **Susan Lowell**
illustrated by **Jim Harris**

AWARD WINNING Book

This is a southwestern adaptation of a familiar folk tale: a chile-flavored "The Three Little Pigs." The story takes place in the Sonoran Desert, where Native American, Mexican, and Anglo cultures blend together.

Javelina (pronounced ha-ve-LEE-na) comes from a Spanish name for the collared peccary, a relative of swine (but not a true pig). Javelinas are extremely bristly—very hairy on the chinny-chin-chin.

ONCE UPON A TIME,

way out in the desert, there were three little javelinas. Javelinas (ha-ve-LEE-nas) are wild, hairy, southwestern cousins of pigs.

Their heads were hairy, their backs were hairy, and their bony legs—all the way down to their hard little hooves—were very hairy. But their snouts were soft and pink.

One day, the three little javelinas trotted away to seek their fortunes. In this hot, dry land, the sky was almost always blue. Steep purple mountains looked down on the desert, where the cactus forests grew.

Soon the little javelinas came to a spot where the path divided, and each one went a different way.

The first little javelina wandered lazily along. He didn't see a dust storm whirling across the desert—until it caught him.

The whirlwind blew away and left the first little javelina sitting in a heap of tumbleweeds. Brushing himself off, he said, "I'll build a house with them!" And in no time at all, he did.

Then along came a coyote. He ran through the desert so quickly and so quietly that he was almost invisible. In fact, this was only one of Coyote's many magical tricks. He laughed when he saw the tumbleweed house and smelled the javelina inside.

"Mmm! A tender juicy piggy!" he thought. Coyote was tired of eating mice and rabbits.

He called out sweetly, "Little pig, little pig, let me come in."

"Not by the hair of my chinny-chin-chin!" shouted the first javelina (who had a lot of hair on his chinny-chin-chin!)

"Then I'll huff, and I'll puff, and I'll blow your house in!" said Coyote.

And he huffed, and he puffed, and he blew the little tumbleweed house away.

But in all the hullabaloo, the first little javelina escaped—and went looking for his brother and sister.

Coyote, who was very sneaky, tiptoed along behind.

The second little javelina walked for miles among giant cactus plants called saguaros (sa-WA-ros). They held their ripe red fruit high in the sky. But they made almost no shade, and the little javelina grew hot.

Then he came upon a Native American woman who was gathering sticks from inside a dried-up cactus. She planned to use these long sticks, called saguaro ribs, to knock down the sweet cactus fruit.

The second little javelina said, "Please, may I have some sticks to build a house?"

"*Ha'u*," (Ha-ou) she said, which means "yes" in the language of the Desert People.

When he was finished building his house, he lay down in the shade. Then his brother arrived, panting from the heat, and the second little javelina moved over and made a place for him.

Pretty soon, Coyote found the saguaro rib house. He used his magic to make his voice sound just like another javelina's.

"Little pig, little pig, let me come in!" he called.

But the little javelinas were suspicious. The second one cried, "No! Not by the hair of my chinny-chin-chin!"

"Bah!" thought Coyote. "I am not going to eat your *hair*."

Then Coyote smiled, showing all his sharp teeth: "I'll huff, and I'll puff, and I'll blow your house in!"

So he huffed, and he puffed, and all the saguaro ribs came tumbling down.

But the two little javelinas escaped into the desert.

Still not discouraged, Coyote followed. Sometimes his magic did fail, but then he usually came up with another trick.

The third little javelina trotted through beautiful palo verde trees, with green trunks and yellow flowers. She saw a snake sliding by, smooth as oil. A hawk floated round and round above her. Then she came to a place where a man was making adobe (a-DOE-be) bricks from mud and straw. The bricks lay on the ground, baking in the hot sun.

The third little javelina thought for a moment, and said, "May I please have a few adobes to build a house?"

"*Sí*," answered the man, which means "yes" in Spanish, the brick-maker's language.

So the third javelina built herself a solid little adobe house, cool in summer and warm in winter. When her brothers found her, she welcomed them in and locked the door behind them.

Coyote followed their trail.

"Little pig, little pig, let me come in!" he called.

The three little javelinas looked out the window. This time Coyote pretended to be very old and weak, with no teeth and a sore paw. But they were not fooled.

"No! Not by the hair of my chinny-chin-chin," called back the third little javelina.

"Then I'll huff, and I'll puff, and I'll blow your house in!" said Coyote. He grinned, thinking of the wild pig dinner to come.

"Just try it!" shouted the third little javelina.

So Coyote huffed and puffed, but the adobe bricks did not budge.

Again, Coyote tried. "I'LL HUFF...AND I'LL PUFF...AND I'LL BLOW YOUR HOUSE IN!"

The three little javelinas covered their hairy ears. But nothing happened. The javelinas peeked out the window.

The tip of Coyote's raggedy tail whisked right past their noses. He was climbing upon the tin roof. Next, Coyote used his magic to make himself very skinny.

"The stove pipe!" gasped the third little javelina. Quickly she lighted a fire inside her wood stove.

"What a feast it will be!" Coyote said to himself. He squeezed into the stove pipe. "I think I'll eat them with red hot chile sauce!"

Whoosh. S-s-sizzle!

Then the three little javelinas heard an amazing noise. It was not a bark. It was not a cackle. It was not a howl. It was not a scream. It was all of those sounds together.

"Yip

    yap

      yeep

        YEE-OWW-OOOOOOOOOOOOO!"

Away ran a puff of smoke shaped like a coyote.

The three little javelinas lived
happily ever after in the adobe house.
And if you ever hear Coyote's voice,
way out in the desert at night. . .well,
you know what he's remembering!

...and still more Pigs

This is the version of *The Three Little Pigs* that many grown-ups probably heard when they were young. Maybe it's the very first one that was told to you, too.

Here's the old story with a new twist. It claims to be the inside lowdown on what *really* took place, as told to the author by none other than A. Wolf.

These pigs live in the Great Smoky Mountains of Appalachia. They seek their fortunes with corn dumplings and hoecakes in their sacks. Instead of a wolf, they've got to be on the lookout for the drooly-mouth fox who just lo-o-o-ves barbecued pig!

Now here's a switch. The wolves in this version of the folk tale are the good guys! They need barbed wire and steel chains to keep out the villain—the very bad pig.

PROJECT

How to
Create a New Episode

Write a story outline for a *new* episode in a series.

Hooray! A new book in your favorite mystery series just arrived in the bookstore. How does the author keep writing new episodes? The answer is simple. It takes imagination and knowing what kids like. You can also find hit series on television, at the movies, in comics, and in cartoons. No matter where you look, there is always a new episode to read or watch.

1 Look at a Series

Put on your thinking cap. It's time to come up with an idea for a new episode in your favorite series. First, choose a fiction series you like. It can be a book, cartoon, or a comic strip series that you read, or a TV, movie, or computer game series that you watch.

TOOLS

- paper and pencil
- markers or colored pencils

Then, take a close look at the series. Answer these questions.

- Who are the main characters?
- Where and when does the series take place?
- Is the series funny, serious, exciting, or scary?

 Tips You can get ideas from:
- **stories you have read.**
- **places you know.**
- **events in your life or someone else's life.**

2 Think of a Story Idea

Create a brand new story for the series you have chosen. Imagine what might happen if:

- the characters go to a new place—a farm, the ocean, a city, outer space, or a park.

- a new character joins the series.

- the characters discover an unusual object, win a contest, or start a business.

Write down your ideas for a new episode. Choose the one you like best.

How Am I Doing?

Before you begin to write your story outline, stop and ask yourself these questions:

- Is the episode about characters in a series?

- Do I know what will happen in the episode?

Now you have an idea for a new episode in your favorite series. Like all good stories, your episode should have a beginning, a middle, and an end. You can tell about the episode by writing a story outline. The outline doesn't have to be long. But it does need to give details about the story.

Here are some things you can include in your story outline:

- a list of the characters and a short description of each

- a couple of sentences telling where and when the episode takes place

- a short description of what happens in the episode

LASSIE:
My Story
By

Julian's Camping Trip
Place: The Beach
Time: Summer
Characters:
Julian
Huey, his b...
Gloria

Julian's Camping Trip

4 Present Your Story

Make an eye-catching cover for the story outline of your new episode. On it, write the series title, the episode's title, and your name.

Then, illustrate the cover with a scene from the story. Place your story outline in the classroom library. Read the story outlines written by your classmates. Did anyone write a new episode for the same series as you did? How are the episodes similar and different?

If You Are Using a Computer ...

Make your episode's cover look really great! Experiment with different kinds and sizes of type for the title and your name. If you use the Sign format, you can place a decorative border around the title page.

CONGRATULATIONS

Now you have become a real hit-series author. Can you spot which new books, TV shows, and movies will become hit series?

Joanna Cole and Bruce Degen
Author and Illustrator ▶

Glossary

a·do·be
(ə dō′bē) *noun*
A sandy kind of clay
used to make bricks.
Sometimes bits of straw
are mixed with the clay.

cac·tus (kak′təs) *noun*
A desert plant that has a
thick stem covered with
sharp spines instead of
leaves.

cam·ou·flaged
(kam′ə fläzhd′)
verb
Disguised or
hidden to
avoid being
easily seen.
▲ **camouflage**

cactus

can·vas
(kan′vəs) *noun*
A heavy, coarse cloth
used for making tents,
sails, and wagon
covers.

chased (chāst) *verb*
Ran after and tried to
catch. The dog *chased*
the ball. ▲ **chase**

chomp (chomp) *verb*
Bite down on. Soon the
rabbit will *chomp* on the
carrot.

com·pli·cat·ed
(kom′pli kā′tid)
adjective
Not easy to understand
or do. The boy couldn't
understand the
complicated directions
for playing the game.

coy·o·te (kī ō′tē)
noun
An animal that looks
like a small, thin wolf.
It lives in North America
and is closely related to
wolves, foxes, and dogs.

dem·on·strate
(dem′ən strāt′) *verb*
Show or explain clearly.
On Mondays, I often
demonstrate how to use
the computer.

coyote

desert

des•ert (dez´ərt) *noun*
A hot, dry, sandy land with little or no plant or animal life.

Word Study

The word **desert** can be pronounced two ways. Each pronunciation has a different meaning. When you say dez´ərt, it means "a hot dry place." When you say di zûrt´, it means "to leave something behind; to abandon."

---

de•tec•tive
(di tek´tiv) *noun*
A person who follows clues to solve a crime.

de•vour
(di vour´) *verb*
Swallow or eat up eagerly. My hungry cats always *devour* their food.

ex•hib•its
(ig zib´its) *noun*
Groups of things that are shown. I saw four *exhibits* of old comic books at the book fair.
▲ **exhibit**

field trip
(fēld´ trip´) *noun*
A trip away from the classroom to learn about something. We took a *field trip* to the museum to study dinosaurs.

ford (fôrd) *noun*
A shallow place where a river can be crossed.

fuz•zy (fuz´ē) *adjective*
Covered with fine, loose fibers or hair. The stuffed bear was soft and *fuzzy*.

gum•shoes
(gum´shoooz´) *noun*
People who find clues and solve mysteries. The *gumshoes* solved three mysteries last month.
▲ **gumshoe**

Word Study

The words *gum* and *shoe* were originally put together to describe *shoe* with *gum*—or rubber— soles. Then **gumshoe** became a slang word for a detective or private eye who goes around quietly on *gum* soled *shoes*.

---

a	add	o͝o	took	ə =
ā	ace	o͞o	pool	a in *above*
â	care	u	up	e in *sicken*
ä	palm	û	burn	i in *possible*
e	end	yo͞o	fuse	o in *melon*
ē	equal	oi	oil	u in *circus*
i	it	ou	pout	
ī	ice	ng	ring	
o	odd	th	thin	
ō	open	th	this	
ô	order	zh	vision	

Glossary

hab·i·tat (hab′i tat′) *noun*
The place where an animal or plant naturally lives and grows. A whale's *habitat* is the ocean.

hitched (hicht) *verb*
Tied or fastened with a rope. She *hitched* the mule to the wagon.
▲ **hitch**

javelina

ja·ve·li·na (hä′və lē′nə) *noun*
A wild pig that lives in the southwestern United States and Mexico; a peccary.

land·scape (land′skāp′) *noun*
A view or scene of surrounding land. The *landscape* was filled with trees and mountains.

lurched (lûrcht) *verb*
Suddenly swayed in one direction or from side to side. The car *lurched* forward and then came to a stop. ▲ **lurch**

par·tic·i·pants (pär tis′ə pənts) *noun*
People who join others in an activity. All the *participants* in the parade wore funny costumes.
▲ **participant**

poi·son·ous (poi′zə nəs) *adjective*
Having a harmful substance that can harm or kill. The bite of a *poisonous* spider can make you very sick.

pray·ing man·tis (prā′ing man′tis) *noun*
An insect with long sticklike legs and a triangle-shaped head. It is related to the grasshopper.

proj·ect (proj′ekt) *noun*
A special study, task, or activity. I collected sea shells for my science *project*.

run·ning gear (run′ing gēr′) *noun*
The part of a wagon that the wheels and steering bar are connected to.

solve (solv) *verb*
To find the answer to a problem or mystery. The detectives will *solve* the crime and catch the criminal.

speck·led (spek′əld) *adjective*
Covered with small dots of different colors. We saw a brown-and-white *speckled* hen.

splash (splash) *verb*
To hit or move through water so that it is thrown about.

praying mantis

stalk•ing (stô´king) *verb*
Following someone or something so as to get close without being seen. The cat was *stalking* a large black beetle.
▲ **stalk**

ta•ble (tā´bəl) *noun*
A piece of furniture with a flat top. It is held up by one or more legs.

Word History

The word **table** comes from a Latin word that means "a board." Long ago, people placed things on boards, just as we put things on *tables* today.

track (trak) *verb*
To follow the footprints or trail of something or someone. The rangers will *track* the bear to its den.

trail (trāl) *noun*
The series of marks or clues left behind by a person or animal. We followed the *trail* of the deer into the forest.

tum•ble•weeds (tum´bəl wedz´) *noun*
Bushy plants that grow in the deserts and plains of western North America. In the autumn, the wind breaks *tumbleweeds* off at their roots and blows them around. ▲ **tumbleweed**

wee•vil (wē´vəl) *noun*
A kind of beetle that feeds on cotton, fruits, and grain. A weevil is usually thought to be a pest by farmers.

a	add	o͝o	took	ə =	
ā	ace	o͞o	pool	a in *above*	
â	care	u	up	e in *sicken*	
ä	palm	û	burn	i in *possible*	
e	end	yo͞o	fuse	o in *melon*	
ē	equal	oi	oil	u in *circus*	
i	it	ou	pout		
ī	ice	ng	ring		
o	odd	th	thin		
ō	open	ᵺ	this		
ô	order	zh	vision		

tumbleweeds

Authors & Illustrators

Jim Harris *pages 108–120*

When this Southwestern artist looks out of his studio window, he sometimes sees elk and other wildlife walking by. And every night he hears the coyotes howl! In the story of *The Three Little Javelinas*, the character named Coyote was inspired by the tales of the Tohono O'Odham tribe. In their traditional stories, Coyote is a trickster who is always getting outsmarted by others!

Ann M. Martin *pages 34–47*

This best-selling author says that she writes her books to entertain herself as well as the young people who read them. When Martin writes a story, she is often reliving memories from her own childhood. When she was young, her parents encouraged her to help others. This attitude is still very important to Ann Martin, and that's one reason why the girls in the Baby-sitters Club are always so active in their community.

Jean Marzollo *pages 62–65*

This author enjoys working on the *I Spy* series because these books are "beautiful and fun at the same time." Walter Wick takes the pictures first, and then Jean Marzollo lets the pictures inspire her to come up with her rhyming riddles. This author has also written rhymes for other books, including the nonfiction books *In 1776* and *In 1492*.

Donald J. Sobol *pages 68–76*

Over 30 years ago, Donald J. Sobol decided to write a mystery book for kids. That book was called *Encyclopedia Brown, Boy Detective*. Sobol wrote the whole book in just two weeks! Since then, he has completed many more books about everyone's favorite boy detective. He's proud that his books offer both challenging mysteries and lots of laughs. Sobol says this about his famous boy detective, "Encyclopedia is the kid I wanted to be when I was ten years old!"

Laura Ingalls Wilder *pages 90–103*

In 1930, a 63-year-old farm woman sat down at her kitchen table to write about her pioneer childhood. That woman was Laura Ingalls Wilder, and her story grew into a series called The Little House books. To Wilder's great surprise, her books became famous. Children all over the world read her stories and kept asking for more. Wilder wrote eight books in all. Laura Ingalls Wilder died in 1957 at the age of 90, but her story lives on in her popular series.

"I lived everything that happened in my books. It is a long story, filled with sunshine and shadow...."

Books &

Author Study

More by Joanna Cole

Bully Trouble
Big Eddie is a bully who is always picking on Arlo and Robby. What can these two friends do to make Eddie stop being a bully?

Scholastic's The Magic School Bus® at the Waterworks
Ride along with Ms. Frizzle and her class as they explore the inner workings of the local waterworks. Laugh at Bruce Degen's great illustrations.

Fiction

Commander Toad in Space
by Jane Yolen
illustrated by Bruce Degen
Brave and Bright. Bright and Brave. Commander Toad and the crew of *Star Warts* travel through space in this science-fiction series.

Henry and Beezus
by Beverly Cleary
Before she wrote about Ramona, Beverly Cleary wrote funny books about Ramona's neighbor, Henry Huggins. In this book, Henry and Beezus become friends when she helps him raise money to buy a new bike.

Julian's Glorious Summer
by Ann Cameron
Julian is the kind of boy who easily finds adventure. In this book, Julian finds lots to do during his summer vacation.

Nonfiction

George Washington Carver: The Peanut Scientist
by Patricia and Fredrick McKissack
What's so special about a peanut? Find out when you read the life story of this great African-American scientist.

. . . If You Lived in Colonial Times
by Ann McGovern
What did people in colonial times wear? This book, and the others in this series, use questions and answers to explain what life was like long ago.

Picture Book of Helen Keller
by David Adler
illustrated by John and Alexandra Wallner
Helen Keller was blind and deaf. With the help of a special teacher, Helen learned to read and write.

&Media

 ## Videos

 ## Software

 ## Magazines

Lassie, Come Home
MGM/UA Home Video
Lassie, the popular dog star, first appeared in this movie. In it, the brave collie journeys hundreds of miles to rejoin the family she loves.
(93 minutes)

Kristy and the Great Campaign
(Baby-sitters Club Videos)
Scholastic Inc./Good Times
In this film, based on the hit series, Kristy decides to help Courtney campaign for president of the third grade.
(30 minutes)

Newton's Apple
Pacific Arts
This award-winning television series makes science fun. Experts answer questions kids have asked about all kinds of topics.
(60 minutes)

Arthur's Teacher Trouble
(Living Book Series)
Broderbund
(Macintosh, CD-ROM)
Arthur the Aardvark is the star of a series of books by Marc Brown. Now you can use this interactive program to join in Arthur's adventures as he prepares for a big spelling bee. This software also lets you choose the language you want to use— English or Spanish.

Super Story Tree
Scholastic Inc. (Apple, IBM)
Write a story, draw pictures, even add music and sound effects! Here's a program that will help you to write and draw a sequel to an existing series, or create a new series of your own.

Spider
Open Court Publishing
This popular magazine contains stories, poems, and articles on all kinds of subjects. It gets its name from a cartoon spider that appears throughout each issue.

DuckTales Magazine
Welsh Publishing Group
Scrooge McDuck and his three nephews star in their own TV series— and in this magazine. This entertainment magazine for kids includes lots of funny stories, comic strips, and puzzles.

A Place to Write

One of Laura Ingalls Wilder's "little houses" is now a museum. For more information about the author and her times, write to:

Laura Ingalls Wilder
Home and Museum
Rocky Ridge Farm
Mansfield, MO 65704

TIME DETECTIVES

Dig into an Archaeological Site

Finding information in stories and artifacts brings the past to life.

Meet the Time Detectives

Archaeologists uncover clues to the past.

ARMOR OF
GEORGE CLIFFORD,
THIRD EARL OF
CUMBERLAND

Blued steel decorated with gold
designs
Made in Greenwich, England,
sometime between 1580 and
1585
Height: 69¼ inches

The third earl of Cumberland
wore this armor when he
attended tournaments. At the
tournaments, knights sh
off their skills. This
was made fr
armor

Look at the Clues

Stories and artifacts provide clues to the past.

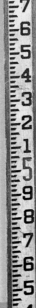

Add Up the Evidence

We can piece together a picture of the past by adding up the evidence.

Trade Books

The following books accompany this *Time Detectives* SourceBook.

Biography

Author

Frederick Douglass Fights for Freedom

by Margaret Davidson

Realistic Fiction

Author/
Illustrator

George Washington's Breakfast

by Jean Fritz
illustrated by
Paul Galdone

Informational Fiction

Author

Let's Go Traveling

by Robin Rector Krupp

Historical Fiction

Book

Three Names

by Patricia MacLachlan
illustrated by
Alexander Pertzoff

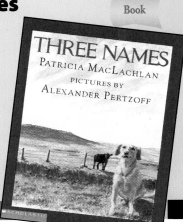

Archaeologists uncover clues to the past.

Meet the Time Detectives

Read a story about a girl who imagines a family's past. Then join real-life kids as they uncover their community's history.

Dig up evidence with archaeologist Ruben Mendoza.

Dive into a treasure hunt— underwater.

WORKSHOP 1

Describe a present-day artifact for time detectives of the future.

ARMOR OF
GEORGE CLIFFORD,
THIRD EARL OF
CUMBERLAND

Blued steel decorated with gold designs
Made in Greenwich, England, sometime between 1580 and 1585
Height: 69½ inches

The third Earl of Cumberland wore this armor when he attended tournaments. At the tournaments, knights showed off their skills. This fancy armor was made for him at the royal armor shops in Greenwich. The Earl dressed in his

9

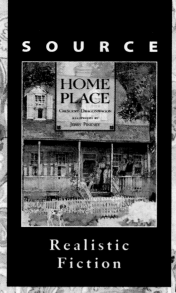
HOME PLACE

BY CRESCENT DRAGONWAGON
ILLUSTRATED BY JERRY PINKNEY

Every year,
these daffodils come up.
There is no house near them.
There is nobody to water them.
Unless someone happens to come this way,
like us, this Sunday afternoon, just walking,
there is not even anyone to see them.
But still they come up, these daffodils
in a row, a yellow splash
brighter than sunlight, or lamplight, or butter,
in the green and shadow of the woods.
Still they come up, these daffodils,
cups lifted to trumpet
the good news
of spring,

though maybe no one hears
except the wind
and the raccoons who rustle at night
and the deer who nibble delicately
at the new green growth
and the squirrels who jump
from branch to branch
of the old black walnut tree.

But once,
someone lived here.
How can you tell?
Look. A chimney, made of stone,
back there, half-standing yet, though honeysuckle's
grown around it—there must
have been a house here. Look.
Push aside these weeds—here's
a stone foundation, laid on earth.
The house once here was built on it.

And if there was a house, there was
a family.
Dig in the dirt, scratch deep, and what
do you find?
A round blue glass marble, a nail.
A horseshoe and a piece
of plate. A small yellow bottle. A china doll's arm.

Listen. Can you listen, back, far back?
No, not the wind, that's now. But listen,
back, and hear:
   a man's voice, scratchy-sweet, singing "Amazing Grace,"
   a rocking chair squeaking, creaking on a porch,
   the bubbling hot fat in a black skillet, the chicken frying,
   and "Tommy! Get in here this minute! If I have to call you
   one more time—!"
   and "Ah, me, it's hot," and "Reckon it'll storm?"
"I don't know, I sure hope, we sure could use it,"
   and "Supper! Supper tiiiiime!"

If you look, you can almost see them:
the boy at dusk, scratching in the dirt with his stick, the
uneven swing hanging vacant
in the black walnut tree, listless in the heat;
the girl, upstairs, combing out her long, long hair, unpinning,
unbraiding, and combing, by an oval mirror;
downstairs, Papa washing dishes as Mama sweeps the floor
and Uncle Ferd, Mama's brother, coming in, whistling, back
from shutting up the chickens
for the night, wiping the sweat
from his forehead.
"Ah, Lord, it's hot, even late as it is,"
"Yes, it surely is."
Someone swats
at a mosquito.
Bedtime.

But in that far-back summer night,
the swing begins to sway
as the wind comes up
as the rain comes down
there's thunder there's lightning (that's just like now)
the dry dusty earth soaks up the water
the roots of the plants, like the daffodil bulbs
the mama planted, hidden under the earth, but alive
and growing, the roots
drink it up. A small green snake
coils happily in the wet woods,
and Tommy sleeps straight through the storm. Anne, the girl, who
wishes for a yellow hair ribbon, wakes and then returns to
sleep, like Uncle Ferd, sighing as he dreams
of walking down a long road with change in his pocket. But
the mother wakes, and wakes the father, her husband,
and they sit on the side of the bed,
and watch the rain together,
without saying a word, in the house where everyone else
still sleeps. Her head on Papa's shoulder,
her long hair falling down her back, she's wearing
a white nightgown
that makes her look
almost like a ghost when the lightning flashes.

And now, she *is* a ghost, and we
can only see her
if we try. We're not sure
if we're making her up, or if
we really can see her, imagining
the home place as it might have been, or was, before
the house burned down, or everyone moved away
and the woods moved in.

Her son and daughter, grown and gone, her brother
who went to Chicago, her husband, even
her grandchildren, even her house,
all gone, almost as gone as if
they had never laughed and eaten chicken and rocked,
played and fought and made up,
combed hair and washed dishes and swept,
sang and scratched at mosquito bites.
Almost as gone, but
not quite. Not quite.
They were here.
This was their home.

For each year, in a quiet green place,
where there's only a honeysuckle-vined chimney
to tell you there was ever a house
(if, that is, you happen to travel that way,
and wonder, like we did);
where there's only a marble, a nail, a horseshoe, a piece
of plate, a piece of doll,
a single rotted almost-gone piece of rope swaying
on a black walnut tree limb,
to tell you there was ever a family here;
only deer and raccoons and squirrels
instead of people
to tell you there were living creatures;
each year, still,
whether anyone sees, or not,
whether anyone listens, or not,
the daffodils come up,
to trumpet their good news
forever and forever.

SOURCE

OWL

Magazine

AWARD WINNING

Magazine

Meet

The Missing Marble Case

Gore Vale mansion, 1925

BOYS CLUB

Many years ago, in 1925, a boy stood on the porch of Gore Vale mansion (see left) with his friends. As he played with a marble in his pocket, it fell out, rolled across the porch, and over the edge into the dirt below. There it stayed until it was found by the team of dirt detectives—over 60 years later!

the Dirt Detectives!

To find out about the mysterious case of Gore Vale mansion, which once stood in Toronto, Canada, George and AnnMarie are searching for clues — clues buried under dirt. Along with professional diggers, they're working on a project to uncover the past. Join them as they dig back through time…

by
Sheila
Fairley

OWL: How did you get interested in digging in the first place?

George: My mom told me about it and so did my uncle who's a teacher.

AnnMarie: I knew a bit about it before coming here with my class, but I had never been on a dig.

Paintbrush for brushing away dirt

Trowel for digging

Meter stick for measuring things you find

Map to record details about where you're digging

Paper bag for storing things you find

Tools of the Trade

OWL: When you first came on the dig, did you have any idea of what you expected to find?

George: I didn't really think I would find anything, but I was lucky. The first day I found a nail, some brick chips and a piece of glass.

OWL: Now that you've worked on this project, has it changed the way you think about the past?

AnnMarie: Before, I thought it was boring, but now I see it's not. We have two hours for a dig but it goes by so fast, it feels like a few minutes!

Measuring tape for measuring larger things

Dustpan for collecting dirt

Whisk broom for cleaning the area you're in

The Story of Gore Vale

1820
Gore Vale mansion is built.

OWL: What's the most interesting thing that you've found while digging?

AnnMarie: I found part of an old china dish. You could only see part of the pattern and it was very colorful.

OWL: Was it different from the kind of dishes that we use today?

AnnMarie: Yes, the china felt like plastic.

OWL: Is there something about digging that you don't like?

George: You have to wait for a long time and you have to go slowly. I would like to be able to go a little faster.

Imagine travelling to another planet and discovering these objects. What do you think they could be used for?

OWL: If you could leave something behind for future diggers to find, what would it be?

AnnMarie: Clothes . . . baggy jeans, and polo shirts.

George: I would probably write a letter or bury a time capsule. I'd write about the things we do.

OWL: What's the most important thing you'd like to share with OWL readers about digging?

George: Don't dig anywhere without checking because it may be against the law—and it could be dangerous!

AnnMarie: If you get a chance, try it—it's really fun. You have to wait, you have to be patient and you never know when something's going to turn up. But when it does, it's a surprise.

1925
Gore Vale is turned into a boy's club and then torn down.

1946
Family housing is built where Gore Vale once stood.

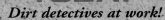
TODAY
Dirt detectives at work!

Dr. Ruben Mendoza

Archaeologist

Archaeology is *fun*. Can *you* dig it?

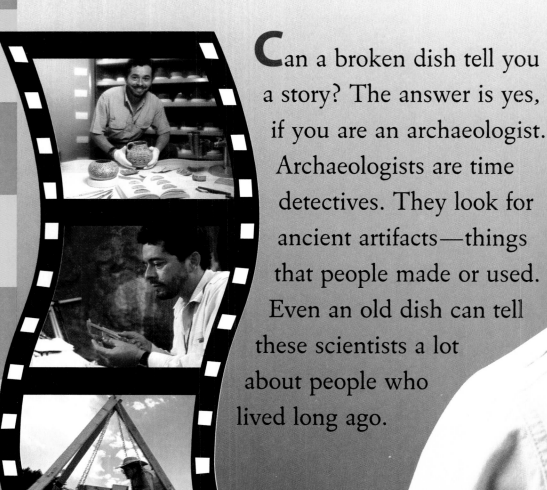

Can a broken dish tell you a story? The answer is yes, if you are an archaeologist. Archaeologists are time detectives. They look for ancient artifacts—things that people made or used. Even an old dish can tell these scientists a lot about people who lived long ago.

PROFILE

Name: Dr. Ruben Mendoza

Born: French Camp, California

Job: assistant professor of archaeology at the University of Colorado

Hobbies: travel and photography

Most exciting find: arrowheads found near Denver, Colorado, that are about 11,000 years old

Where he would go if he were a time traveler: back in time 1,400 years to an ancient city in Mexico

QUESTIONS

for Dr. Ruben Mendoza

Here's *how one* time detective, **Dr. Ruben Mendoza,** finds *clues* to the past.

 How did you become interested in archaeology?

 I went on a trip to Mexico when I was twelve. I became fascinated by the pyramids there. Being Mexican-American, I thought about the forgotten people who had built them. I even wondered if one of my ancestors had worked on them.

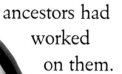

 Weren't you recently on an archaeological trip in Mexico?

 Yes, I went with a group of archaeologists and students. We were on a dig. We use that word because we dig up things from the past.

 What is the first thing you do on a dig?

 Before we do any digging, we lay a grid of string over the whole area. Then we make a paper map showing the same thing. That way, we can record on the map where each artifact is found.

How do you know where to start digging?

 We look for clues. We might start at a circle of stones that could be the remains of an old fireplace. Or we might dig into a mound—a small hill. This could be a spot where people left things behind.

 What do you learn from clues found on a dig?

 Sometimes we find stone knives and bone needles. These show that ancient people knew how to make and use tools.

 Are all artifacts found underground?

 No. Sometimes we find petroglyphs. They're drawings, usually found on a rock cliff or on the wall of a cave. They often picture animals that lived in the area.

 What do you do with artifacts you find on a dig?

 Each artifact is given a number, then weighed and measured. Drawings and maps are photographed. We write all these facts on a card, along with the date, place, and name of the person who found it. Later, this information goes into a computer file so it's easy for others to study. The artifacts themselves end up in a museum.

Dr. Ruben Mendoza's
Tips for Young Archaeologists

1 If you find an artifact, record exactly where you found it.

2 Study the place where you discovered the artifact. Read about the people who once might have lived there.

3 Give the artifact to a museum. Take along the records you have kept.

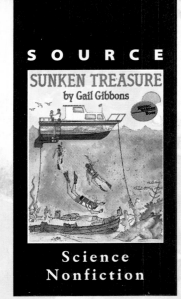

SOURCE

SUNKEN TREASURE
by Gail Gibbons

Science
Nonfiction

from

SUNKEN

by Gail Gibbons

AWARD
WINNING

Book

"It's there! It's really there!"

The rotting hull of a ship has been found
on the ocean floor. Within the wreck lies a
fabulous treasure.

The story of each underwater treasure hunt
is different, but each goes back to the same
beginning . . . the sinking of a ship. The story of
the hunt for the *Nuestra Señora de Atocha*, a
Spanish galleon, begins the same way.

TREASURE

THE ATOCHA

The Sinking

It is 1622. The *Atocha*, with its fleet of sister ships, makes its way back from South America to Spain. The *Atocha* is a treasure ship, laden with gold, jewels, silver bars, and thousands of coins.

The fleet makes a stop in Cuba and then sets off again. As the ships near Florida, a hurricane gathers strength.

Wind rips at the *Atocha*'s sails. Spray washes across the deck. The 265 people aboard the ship are terrified. Suddenly, a huge wave lifts the ship and throws it against a reef.

The hull breaks open, and the *Atocha*—along with several of its sister ships—sinks beneath the waves. All but five aboard the *Atocha* drown.

The Search

Spain wants its treasure back. Search ships are sent out. They find one of the *Atocha*'s sister ships, the *Santa Margarita*, and salvage begins. Sponge and pearl divers bring some of the *Santa Margarita*'s treasure to the surface.

But the *Atocha* cannot be found.

Hundreds of years go by. The *Atocha* is almost forgotten. Storms and strong sea currents scatter its treasure for miles along the ocean floor. The ship slowly rots and breaks into pieces. Sand covers the remains.

In the early 1960's, a new search begins. A man named Mel Fisher has read about the *Atocha*. He is determined to find the lost treasure ship. He will need boats, crew, and equipment. Investors provide the money, and the venture gets under way.

Search boats go to where it is believed the *Atocha* went down.

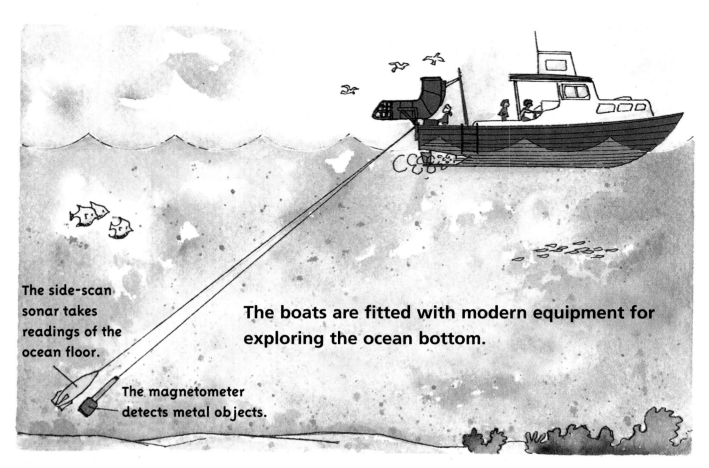

The side-scan sonar takes readings of the ocean floor.

The magnetometer detects metal objects.

The boats are fitted with modern equipment for exploring the ocean bottom.

air tank

The underwater metal detector locates metal objects, too.

When the instruments register a "hit," divers go down to investigate. They keep in view of each other and regularly check their air supplies.

mailboxes

Large elbow-shaped pipes, called mailboxes, are swung into place. The mailboxes are Mel Fisher's invention. The whirling of the boat's propellers forces water through the mailboxes, blowing large holes in the sand. If anything is buried, it will be uncovered.

But only litter is found—nothing of value, nothing from the *Atocha*.

Where should they look next?

Mel Fisher asks for help from Eugene Lyon, an expert who can translate old Spanish documents. Lyon looks through stacks of shipping records from the 1600's. The work takes years.

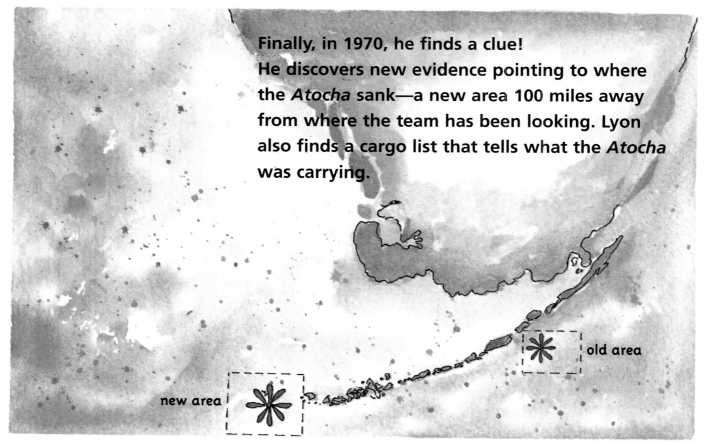

Finally, in 1970, he finds a clue! He discovers new evidence pointing to where the *Atocha* sank—a new area 100 miles away from where the team has been looking. Lyon also finds a cargo list that tells what the *Atocha* was carrying.

old area

new area

A search boat moves to the new location.

In 1971, a huge galleon anchor, several muskets, and gold bars and chains are found. But are they from the *Atocha*? There is no way to prove it.

Two years later, three heavy silver bars are recovered. The bars with their markings match up with the *Atocha*'s cargo list. Now they have proof!

Then, in 1975, the *Atocha*'s bronze cannons are found. The crew believe they are getting closer to the mother lode . . . the main treasure of the ship.

But they are wrong. Day after day they search the huge area. Many more years go by. Crew members leave and new ones sign on. When the money runs out, new investors must be found.

The Find

1985. The crew go back and search a site they had searched years ago. And then it happens—a big "hit" registers on their equipment. Divers go down.

"We found it! The mother lode!"

Mel Fisher's twenty-year search is finally over. Resting on the ocean floor, 55 feet below, is the *Atocha*'s fabled treasure—glinting gold bars, jewelry, gold and silver coins, and other precious finds. Nearly all the listed cargo is there, and more—some treasure must have been smuggled aboard.

The Recording

The crew works with a marine archaeologist, Duncan Mathewson. He insists that the mother lode not be disturbed. A grid of plastic pipes is laid over the site.

underwater camera

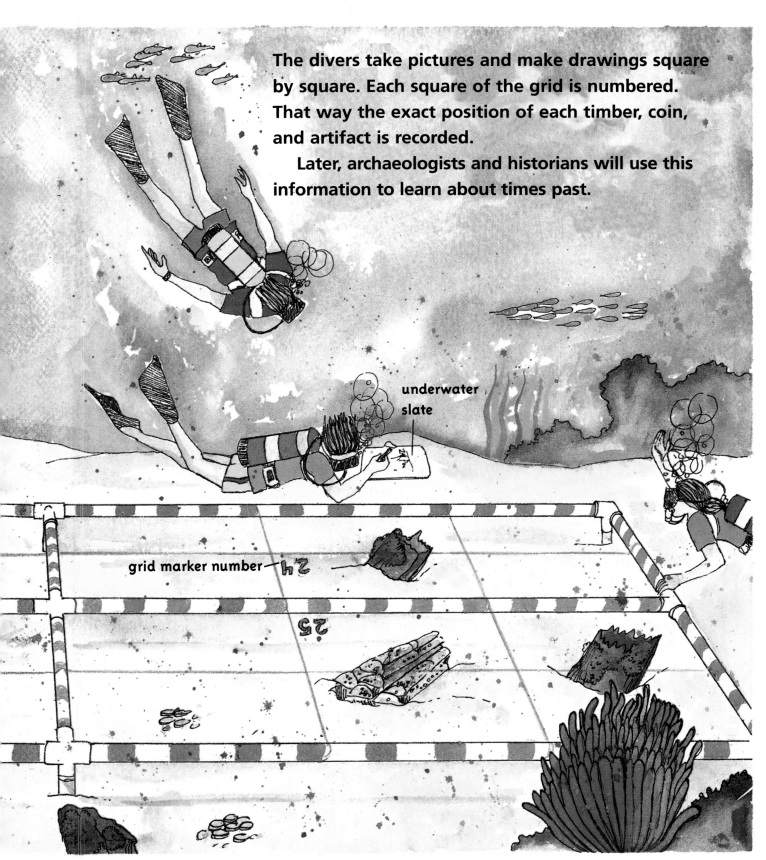

The divers take pictures and make drawings square by square. Each square of the grid is numbered. That way the exact position of each timber, coin, and artifact is recorded.

Later, archaeologists and historians will use this information to learn about times past.

underwater slate

grid marker number

The Salvage

Now the treasure can be brought to the surface. Salvage boats are moved in. Divers descend and crew members lower baskets over the side to them.

The divers gently fan the sand with their hands and use an airlift to carefully suck it away.

airlift

As treasure is recovered, other artifacts are exposed underneath. Each piece of treasure must be accounted for. Again, everything found is sketched and photographed.

One after another, baskets full of treasure are raised to the surface.

Each day the work continues . . . dive after dive after dive. More treasure is recovered from the deep. It is hard work and can be done only in good weather.

The salvage goes on for weeks, months, and years.

Restoration and Preservation

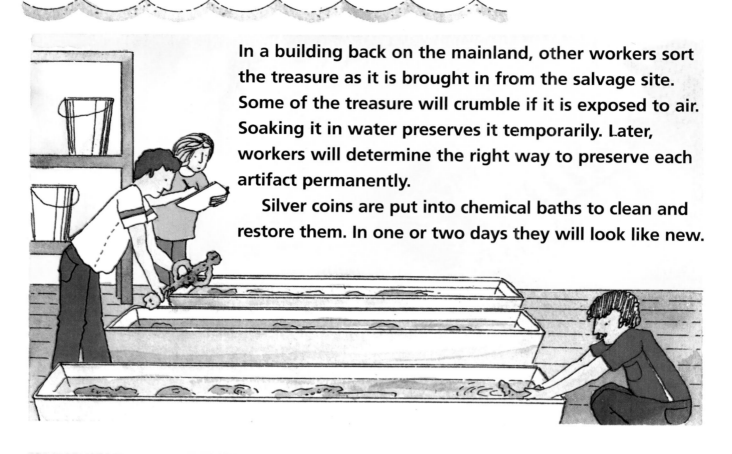

In a building back on the mainland, other workers sort the treasure as it is brought in from the salvage site. Some of the treasure will crumble if it is exposed to air. Soaking it in water preserves it temporarily. Later, workers will determine the right way to preserve each artifact permanently.

Silver coins are put into chemical baths to clean and restore them. In one or two days they will look like new.

Silver bars soak in chemical baths, too, but they will take longer to clean. They are bigger. The gold from the *Atocha* is already shiny—gold never loses its luster.

There were many pottery storage jars on board the *Atocha*. Amazingly, some are recovered whole. Other jars had been shattered and now must be pieced together again.

Cataloging

Cataloging of the *Atocha's* treasure is done in several ways:

A photographer takes pictures of a sword.

Coins are scanned by a computer, and an exact description of each one is stored in the computer's memory.

An artist draws pictures of a gold plate and an emerald-studded necklace.

This kind of careful cataloging provides a valuable record for the future.

Distribution

Some of the treasure will go to museums.

Some will go to the investors and some will go to the crew. All of them made it possible for Mel Fisher's long search to continue. A computer works out what each one's fair share will be.

The treasure of the *Nuestra Señora de Atocha* is valued at hundreds of millions of dollars . . . a very wealthy treasure ship indeed!

The wreck and its artifacts will be studied by historians and archaeologists for years to come. Their discoveries will enrich our knowledge of the past. This will be the second treasure of the *Atocha*.

How to Create an Artifact Exhibit Card

artifact described in the card

How do you learn about the past? One way is to look at artifacts in a museum. You might discover a toy from ancient Egypt or an arrowhead made thousands of years ago. To learn more about each artifact, you can read the exhibit card that goes with it.

What is an exhibit card? An exhibit card gives information about an artifact—when it was made, who made it, what it was made of, and how it was used.

name of artifact

size

ARMOR OF GEORGE CLIFFORD, THIRD EARL OF CUMBERLAND

Blued steel decorated with gold designs

Made in Greenwich, England, sometime between 1580 and 1585

Height: 69½ inches

The third earl of Cumberland wore this armor when he attended tournaments. At the tournaments, knights showed off their skills. This fancy armor was made for him at the royal armor shops in Greenwich. When the earl dressed in his armor, he had to put on fourteen different pieces. They were held together with leather straps. Each piece was made of strong plates of steel held together with metal pins. This made the armor flexible, so the earl could move easily.

This armor was purchased by the Muncie Fund in 1932.

materials used

where and when artifact was made

description—includes interesting details

information about how the museum acquired the artifact

1 Choose an Artifact

Think of all the different kinds of "artifacts" you use in a day, at home or at school. They might be for eating, traveling, doing schoolwork, playing sports, or getting ready for bed. They might be in-line skates, a fancy pencil, or a baseball cap. Choose an artifact that you would like to see in a museum.

TOOLS

- paper and pencil
- large index card
- an artifact

2 Collect Information

Gather as much information as you can about your artifact. What is it? How is it used? Where was it made? Where is it used? What is it made of? Who uses it? Is there anything unusual about it? Does it have any decorations? Keep notes on your discoveries.

Tips
- Look at the artifact carefully.
- Think of what you already know about it.
- Read labels and any writing on it.
- Read about it in a reference book.

3 Write Your Card

Use the information you've gathered to write your exhibit card.

- On the index card, write the artifact's name.
- Below the name, write a short paragraph about the artifact.
- Include interesting facts.

Place your artifact with its exhibit card.

4 Create an Exhibit

With your classmates, set up a museum exhibit called "Things We Use." Put artifacts that are similar together. For example, artifacts about school might go in one group. Artifacts about hobbies might go in another. Display each artifact with its exhibit card. Now tour your museum. Look at all the artifacts. What did you discover about the time you live in?

If You Are Using a Computer ...

Create your exhibit card using the Poster format. Browse through the collection of clip art for an artifact to show on your card. Choose an attractive border to make your card complete.

THINK

Imagine that you could travel a hundred years into the future. What artifacts from today do you think you might find?

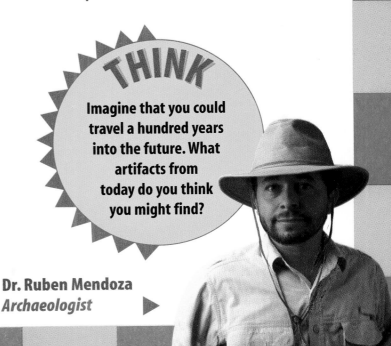

Dr. Ruben Mendoza
Archaeologist ▶

Look at the Clues

Discover what 26 amazing artifacts—from A to Z—tell us about the past.

Meet a young Pueblo storyteller and share her favorite legend about her people.

WORKSHOP 2

Search for clues to the past in an old picture.

CLUES
to the
PAST
A to Z

by
Patricia and Fredrick McKissack

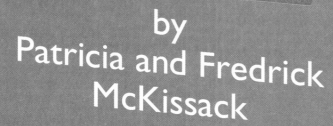

AWARD WINNING

Authors

This is a book of artifacts. An artifact is an object from the past that can tell us something about the people who made and used it.

Follow the alphabet from A to Z to learn about 26 artifacts and their stories.

Happy exploring!

Arrowhead

Long ago, people used bows and arrows to hunt and wage war. They usually made arrowheads from materials such as shells, rocks, and bones found near their homes. Native Americans west of the Rocky Mountains probably shaped these arrowheads. The rocks they're made from are plentiful there.

Basket

Baskets were among the first objects people learned to make. They were beautiful as well as useful. These sea grass baskets were woven by African Americans. Their slave ancestors brought the art of basket making from Africa. They passed the skill down to their children and grandchildren.

Coin

Coins often give us information about the past. This one-dollar coin was issued between 1979 and 1981 by the United States government. It honors Susan B. Anthony. During the 19th century, she worked for an end to slavery and for the right of women to vote.

Doll

We know that children have played with dolls for the last 3,000 years. This doll was found in an ancient Egyptian tomb. It gives us an idea of how Egyptian children dressed and wore their hair long ago.

Eyeglasses

This painting of Benjamin Franklin tells us an interesting story about eyeglasses. The famous inventor is wearing bifocals, which are special glasses that he designed in 1784.

Fabric

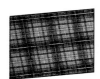

Long ago in Scotland, all the great families wore clothing made from specially designed fabric called tartan. You could tell which family a person belonged to by the tartan he or she wore. Today, Scots still wear their family tartan. But tartan plaids have also become popular with people all over the world.

Game

Yes, children played jacks and marbles over 3,000 years ago. Knucklebones was the ancient Greek form of jacks. And Roman children played with colored glass and pottery marbles.

Hat

the last drop from his STETSON

In the American West, the cowboy's hat was more than a fashion craze. Cowboys used their hats to water their horses, and also as fans, umbrellas, drinking cups, and even as pillows.

Ice skates

Ice skates like these were popular with Americans in the 1860s. The ankle strap was a new addition at that time. It helped people keep their balance.

Journal

Many travelers keep journals. Journals help us see a place as the traveler saw it. Meriwether Lewis and William Clark explored the land northwest of the Mississippi River between 1804 and 1806. Each of them kept a journal.

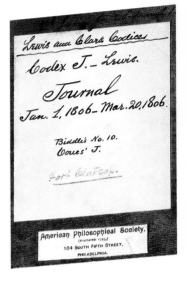

Kite

The Chinese were the first to make and fly kites. Their kites help us learn about Chinese culture and traditions. The Chinese flew kites to celebrate births, marriages, holidays, and festivals. The butterfly kite is one of the oldest and most popular designs.

Lamp

In the 1800s, before electric lights were invented, many people used gas lamps to light their homes. Gas lamps were also used to light the streets at night.

Map

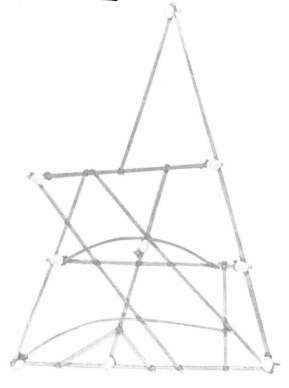

Long ago, people from the Marshall Islands made very accurate maps from grass reeds and sea shells. They used these maps to travel from island to island in the huge Pacific Ocean. Each cowrie shell marks the location of an island. The reed sticks show the direction of the waves between the islands.

Newspaper

Old newspapers are a great source of information about the past. *The New York Times* began publishing in 1851. It has kept a running diary of the day-to-day activities of ordinary and extraordinary people since the first day it went to press. What were the headlines on the day you were born?

Olla

For hundreds of years, Native Americans of the Southwest made clay jars called *ollas* (OH-yuz) to carry water to their homes. Ollas are still being made. Today they are sometimes used as water jars. But more often, they are collected as beautiful works of art.

Portrait

Every American president has been painted or photographed. Abraham Lincoln's portraits are among the most well known. These two photographs show how much he changed from the time he took office in 1861 until his death in 1865.

◀ 1861

1865 ▶

Quilt

This bride's quilt, from the 1850s, shows scenes from the bride's life. It tells the personal story of her courtship, engagement, and even her hopes and dreams for the future. When quilts are passed down from one generation to another, so are their stories.

Rug

The desert nomads of Persia were among the earliest known rug makers. They used their beautiful rugs in their daily lives. Persian carpets became very popular in Europe in the 1400s. Europeans used the one-of-a-kind rugs as wall hangings or table covers. They rarely used them on the floor!

Sundial

How did people tell time before there were clocks or watches? They often used sundials—sometimes portable ones like this one! The position of the sun's shadow on the dial showed the time. What happened when it was cloudy? People made a good guess.

Toy

Teddy bears are one of the best-loved toys in the world. They were named after President Theodore "Teddy" Roosevelt. In 1902, toymaker Morris Michtom saw a cartoon showing the President unwilling to shoot a bear cub. He made the toy teddy bear to honor the President.

Umbrella

The umbrella is an item we use to keep dry in the rain. But for the Asante people of West Africa, the umbrella was—and still is—a symbol of the king's power. There were hundreds of royal umbrellas. Each one had a special meaning. For example, when a king sat under an umbrella topped with a hen and baby chicks, it meant he was a judge settling arguments.

Vacuum cleaner

This is not an early fire engine! It's the original vacuum cleaner, invented in England in 1901. Men in uniform pulled it down city streets and offered to vacuum people's rugs. The machine remained on the street, and the hose was put through a window.

Weathervane and Whirligig

For many centuries people have wanted to know, "Which way is the wind blowing and how fast?" Long before there were TV weather forecasters, people put weathervanes and whirligigs on poles, rooftops, fences, and mailboxes to keep track of wind direction and speed. Today these objects are often used as decorations.

X-chair

The X-chair is one of the oldest kinds of folding furniture. The ancient Egyptians and Romans were the first to use X-chairs. They were easy for soldiers and hunters to carry. Later, European furniture makers called the X-chair a "scissor chair." Can you see why?

Yarn painting

The Huichol people of Mexico are known for their colorful yarn paintings. Each picture shows things that are important to the Huichol way of life—the sun, corn, sheep. For hundreds of years, these beautiful designs were painted or carved on rocks. Then the Huichol began to make their pictures with yarn.

Zither

Zithers were first made in China thousands of years ago. Different designs spread all over the world. During the early 1700s, zithers like this one were brought to America by European immigrants. The zither is one of the instruments that gives Appalachian music its twangy sound.

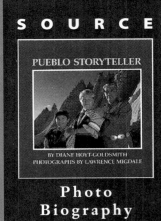

from

Pueblo Storyteller

BY DIANE HOYT-GOLDSMITH
PHOTOGRAPHS BY LAWRENCE MIGDALE

My name is April. I live with my grandparents in the Cochiti (KOH-chi-tee) Pueblo near Santa Fe, New Mexico. Pueblo (PWEB-loh) is a Spanish word that means "village" or "town." Our pueblo is very old. The Cochiti people have lived on these lands for many hundreds of years.

For me there is a special time at the end of every day. After the work is finished and I am ready to go to bed, my grandmother and grandfather tell me stories from the past. Sometimes they tell about the legends of the pueblo people. Other times they tell about things that happened in their own lives.

My grandmother likes to tell about when she was a girl. She lived in a Tewa (*TAY-wah*) pueblo to the north called San Juan. She remembers autumn, a time when her whole family worked together to harvest and husk the corn crop. The corn came in many colors—red and orange, yellow and white, blue and purple, and even the deepest black.

Her family would sit in the shade of a ramada (*rah-MAH-dah*) built of cedar branches. Sheltered from the hot sun, the workers would remove the husks from a mountain of colorful corn. All the time they were working, they would laugh at jokes, sing songs, and share stories.

My grandmother tells me there were always lots of children around—her brothers and sisters, their cousins and friends—and they always had fun. My grandfather tells how the boys would use their slingshots to hurl stones at the crows who came too close to the corncobs that were drying in the sun.

As I listen to their stories, I can almost hear the sound of laughter as the children play at their games. I can smell the bread baking as the women prepare to feed their families. I can see the mounds of corn, colored like the rainbow, drying in the sun.

When I was very young, my grandparents told me a legend about how our ancestors found the place where we are living today, our pueblo along the Rio Grande River. They call it "How the People Came to Earth," and it is still one of my favorite tales.

How the People Came to Earth

◀◀◀◀◆▶▶▶▶

A PUEBLO LEGEND

Long, long ago, our people wandered from place to place across the universe. Their leader was Long Sash, the star that we call Orion. He was the great warrior of the skies. Long Sash told his people that he had heard of a land far away, a place where they could make a home.

Because the people were weary of wandering, they decided to follow Long Sash on the dangerous journey across the sky to search for a new home. They traveled on the Endless Trail, the river of countless stars that we call the Milky Way.

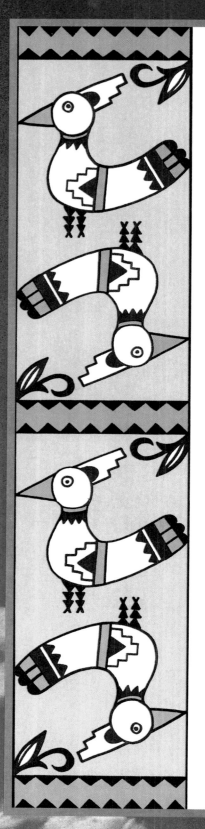

The way was hard for our people. Long Sash taught them to hunt for food, and to make clothing from the skins of animals and the feathers of birds. Even so, they were often hungry and cold, and many died along the way. Long Sash led them farther than any people had ever gone before.

After a time, the people came to a vast darkness, and they were afraid. But Long Sash, the great warrior, believed they were heading the right way, and led them on. Suddenly, they heard the faint sound of scratching. Then, as they watched, a tiny speck of light appeared in the distance. As they got nearer, the light grew larger and larger. Then they saw that it was a small hole leading to another world.

When they looked through the opening, they saw a little mole digging away in the earth. Long Sash thanked the mole for helping them to find their way out of the darkness. But the mole only replied, "Come in to our world. And when you see the sign of my footprints again, you will know you have found your true home." The people saw a cord hanging down from the hole and they all climbed up and went through into the new world.

Once through the opening, Long Sash saw Old Spider Woman busily weaving her web. He asked permission to pass through her house. Old Spider Woman replied, "You may come through my house. But when you next see the sign of my spiderweb, you will have found your true home."

The people did not understand what Old Spider Woman meant, but they thanked her and continued on their journey.

Long Sash and his followers traveled to many places on the earth. They found lands of ice and snow, lands where the sun burned and the air was dry, and beautiful lands with tall trees and plenty of game for hunting. In all of these places, they searched for signs of the mole and Old Spider Woman, but found nothing.

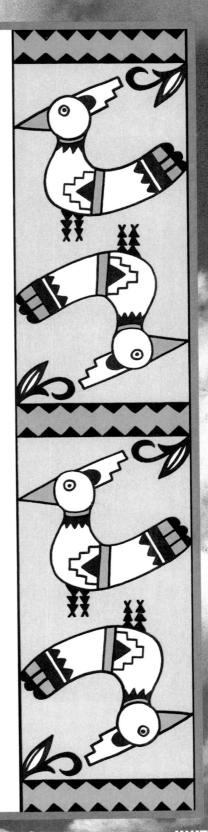

Some of the people stayed behind in the lands they discovered, but Long Sash and most of the tribe kept going. They kept searching for their true home.

Finally they came to a new land where the seasons were wet and dry, hot and cold, with good soil and bad. They found, here and there, small tracks that looked like a mole's. They followed the tracks and found a strange-looking creature, with ugly, wrinkled skin. The slow-moving animal carried a rounded shell on its back.

Long Sash was very happy when he saw the creature. "Look!" he said. "He carries his home with him, as we have done these many years. He travels slowly, just like us. On his shell are the markings of the spiderweb and his tracks look just like the mole's."

When our people saw the turtle, they knew they had found the homeland they had traveled the universe to discover. And we still live on those same lands today.

My grandparents are storytellers who have brought the past alive for me through their memories, through their language, through their art, and even through the food we eat. I am thankful that they have given me this rich history. From them I have learned to bake bread in an ancient way, to work with the earth's gift of clay, and to dance to the music of the Cochiti drums.

I am a pueblo child and I love to listen to my grandparents tell stories. From their example, I learn to take what I need from the earth to live, but also how to leave something behind for future generations. Every day I am learning to live in harmony with the world. And every day, I am collecting memories of my life to share one day with my own children and grandchildren.

How to Discover Picture Clues

How can we learn about people who lived 50, 100, or even 500 years ago? One way is to look for picture clues in old paintings or photographs.

What are picture clues? Picture clues are the details you see in paintings and photographs. These special clues show what life was like long ago—how people dressed, how they traveled, what they ate, and even what they did for fun.

Clothing was different from that worn by people today.

Horses were used for transportation.

The one-room schoolhouse was made of logs.

There were no other buildings nearby.

The children were different ages.

In Colorado during the late 1800s, children rode horses to school every day. Students in grades 1 through 8 all studied together in a one-room log cabin—and one teacher taught them all.

The caption tells about the photo.

1 Find a Picture

In your library, find an old picture with lots of details. It can be a photograph, a drawing, or a painting. Look in books and magazines. If you need help, ask your librarian. Or ask your family to find an old picture at home.

TOOLS

- old painting or photograph
- notebook
- pencil
- magnifying glass (optional)

2 Look for Clues

Look carefully at your picture. Take notes on what you see. These questions may help you.

- When was the picture taken?
- What place does it show?
- Who are the people in the picture?
- What are they wearing?
- What are they doing?

Do you notice anything else—toys, food, furniture, kinds of transportation?

3 Organize Your Notes

Scientists like Dr. Ruben Mendoza organize their notes. It helps them write about what they have found. You can use a chart to organize your notes about the old picture you looked at.

Place Colorado Time late 1800s

Things People Used	How People Traveled	What People Wore
Candles	horseback wagon	long dresses highbutton shoes big hats

Tip A chart can help you put similar details together.

4 Write a Caption

Now you can tell the world about the picture you chose. Look at your notes and chart. Decide which details are most important. Then write an informational caption that tells what is happening in the picture. Share the picture and caption with your classmates. Tell them what you discovered about the past.

If You Are Using a Computer...

Use your Newsletter format on the computer to make your organizing chart. Create columns and headings to help order your notes. If you like, you may also write the caption for your picture using a special font.

THINK

Archaeologists look at pictures for clues about how people once lived. What would a photograph of your classroom tell about school today?

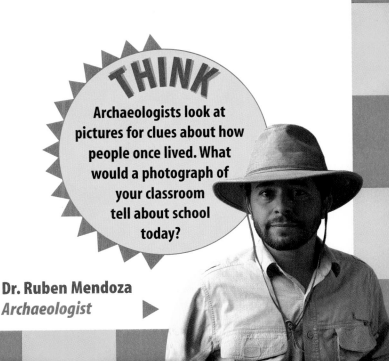

Dr. Ruben Mendoza
Archaeologist ▶

We can piece together a picture of the
past by adding up the evidence.

Add Up the Evidence

Learn what life was like
at the time of the great
woolly mammoths.

Find out what a time
capsule reveals about
life 75 years ago.

Discover what
tomorrow's children
might think about
life today.

PROJECT

Make your own time capsule for
future archaeologists.

FROM
WILD AND WOOLLY
MAMMOTHS

BY
ALIKI

AWARD
WINNING

Author

Mammoths were the giant land mammals of their time.

They roamed quietly in groups.

Mammoths were peaceful plant eaters.

They did not have to hunt other animals for food.

But they had enemies.

One was the fierce saber-toothed tiger.

There were other enemies, too.
Man was the mammoth's greatest enemy.
Inside dark, damp caves scientists found out
   how important the mammoth was to early man.

They discovered paintings of mammoths on cave walls.

They found clay figures and bone carvings of mammoths and other animals.

They knew no animal made them.

They were made by early people who lived in the caves.

They were made in the days of the mammoth hunters, more than 25,000 years ago.

These hunters used tools made of stone, so we call their time the Stone Age.

These are some of the things found in caves in France.

Woolly mammoth carved in stone

This little horse was carved about 30,000 years ago from the tusk of a mammoth.

a carved mammoth

Bone knife carved with bison and plants.

A whole Stone Age village was found in Czechoslovakia and dug up.

Archaeologists, who are scientists who study ancient ruins, learned a lot from this village and others like it.

They learned more about mammoth hunters and how they lived.

This is what they found out.

Mammoth hunters left the caves where they lived in the winter.

In the spring they moved to river valleys where herds of
  mammoths roamed.

They made tents in the valleys to be near the mammoths.

Stone Age men made remarkable tools. They hit one stone with another until it had a sharp edge or point.

hand-axe   cleaver   double-edged scraper

chopping tool   borer   spearhead

The mammoth hunters made knives and other tools of stone.
They used wooden spears with sharp stone points to kill the
    mammoths.
But first they had to trap them.
Sometimes the hunters made fires around the herds.
Then they forced the frightened mammoths down steep cliffs.
Other hunters waited at the bottom to kill the mammoths with
    their spears.

Sometimes the mammoth
   hunters dug deep pits.
They covered the pits with
   branches and earth.

When a mammoth
   walked over the pit,
   the branches broke,
   and the mammoth fell in.

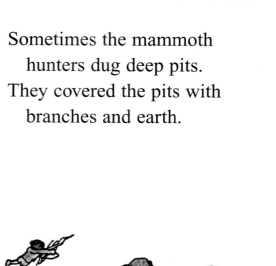

It could not escape.
Hunters rolled heavy stones
down on it and killed the
trapped mammoth.

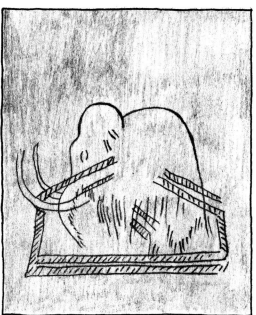

Many mammoths found showed that
their bones had been broken.

This Stone Age painting
was found on a wall
in a cave in France.

Some people think
it shows a mammoth
caught in a pit trap.

The hunters and their families ate the mammoth meat.
They crushed the skulls and ate the brains.

They used the bones to
make tent frames.

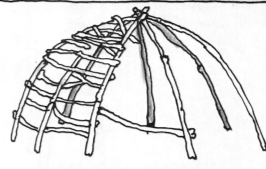

Then the bones were probably covered
with the skins of other animals.

They burned bones
for fuel, too.

The fat from inside the bones
oozed out and kept the fire burning.

They used bones and tusks
to make jewelry.

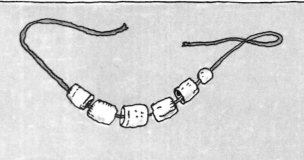

Necklace beads found in Czechoslovakia
were carved from mammoth tusks.

The earliest musical
instruments we know about
were made of mammoths'
bones and tusks.
But their skin was too tough
for anything.

These people hunted other animals, too.
The woolly rhinoceros and the giant sloth lived then.

Today they are extinct.

But bison, reindeer, horses, and foxes, which also lived then, have not died out.

Mammoths were hunted for a long time.

There were plenty of them, and one mammoth was enough to feed many families.

Today there are no mammoths.

Some people think it was the mammoth hunters who killed them all.

Perhaps they died out when the climate grew too warm.

No one knows.

But not one live woolly mammoth has been seen for 11,000 years.

SOURCE

Cricket

Magazine

MY FATHER'S GRANDFATHER AND THE  TIME MACHINE

by **Staton Rabin**

illustrated by **Gail Piazza**

Last week when the winter sky was blue like a robin's egg, we rode a rickety train into the city. The train went one way, and the seats on it faced the other. So, backwards we went, at forty miles an hour, my father's grandfather and I—rattling all the way.

"Will you hold my hand in the city?" Grandpa asked me.
The train wiggled and made us sway from side to side. He
whispered in my ear, "I'm afraid of the alligators."

"Well . . . O.K.," I said. "But there aren't any alligators, and
you know it. *Now* will you tell me why we're going to the city?"

"We're going back in time," my father's grandfather said.
"We're taking a trip in a time machine."

And that's all he would tell me until we finally stood on a checkered stone floor inside a tall building. I was glad to be out of the cold, but why had we come in here? There was nothing to see or do—just a big, stone room that made my voice echo when I talked.

"O.K., where's the time machine?" I asked impatiently.

Grandpa looked at his watch and said, "Close your eyes."

"This is silly," I told him, but I closed my eyes. He led me somewhere by the hand and then said, "Open them."

I did, but I still didn't see a time machine—just a few old people standing around in a group. One old man was kneeling on the floor with a crowbar in his hand. He was prying a heavy brass circle from the floor.

"What's he doing?" I whispered to Grandpa.

"He's opening the time capsule," he whispered back.

"Is that like a pill for when you're sick?"

"Very funny," my father's grandfather said.

With a final grunt, the old man lifted the brass circle from the floor. The others applauded and cheered in scratchy old voices. Then one of them reached into the deep hole in the floor that had been covered by the brass circle and gently lifted out a metal box. Slowly the man opened it, and we crowded around to see what was inside.

What a disappointment! There was just a bunch of old junk in the box.

"Grandpa! You brought me here to see junk?" I said a bit too loudly. "Why would anyone want to bury some junk in the floor?"

The old people turned to stare at me, and I was a little embarrassed.

"Young lady," one of the old men said to me. He wasn't smiling. "People bury a time capsule so that people who come after them, a long time after they're gone, can dig it up and learn what life was really like for them. What the world was like long ago. A time capsule says: This is who we were. This is how we want to be remembered."

"Oh," I said. "So what do you put in a time capsule?"

"Everyday things," the old man replied, wiping his nose with a large, wrinkled handkerchief.

"Like a handkerchief?"

"And why not? Ordinary things. Not-so-ordinary things. Anything that will last a while. Not what you ate for lunch today. I'd hate to be the one to dig up your tuna fish sandwich a thousand years from now."

"I had peanut butter for lunch," I said.

The old man smiled.

I turned to Grandpa. "How do you know when it's time to dig it up, Grandpa? The time capsule, I mean."

"Sometimes it's whenever people think it's time," he said. "Or when somebody notices it's there after years of not noticing. But, sometimes, the time capsule tells you when to open it."

"And this one?" I asked.

"They're going to tear this building down," he said. "So now's the time to open the capsule, don't you think?"

"What's the number on it mean?"

"That's the year the capsule was buried. Seventy-six years ago."

The old people were busily looking through the items in the box. We looked over their shoulders.

There was an old machine in it. Grandpa told me it was a radio. . . . Some newspaper clippings and an x-ray of somebody's lungs. Grandpa explained that x-rays and radios were pretty new in 1915. There was also a shoe in the box—

but not the kind you see every day—a horseshoe! There
were a few other things in the time capsule, but I was most
interested in a photograph that Grandpa had pulled from the
bottom of the box.

"See the kid in the round glasses and the short pants?" he
said, pointing to a boy in the photo.

"Pretty nerdy!" I said. "Did everyone dress like that?"

"Watch what you say about your grandpa," he said,
laughing.

"Grandpa! *You* put the photo in the time capsule!"

"That's your great-great-grandma Maggie, standing next to
me," he said, pointing to the tall, skinny woman in the photo.
I'd never seen a picture of her before. She was my father's
grandfather's mother. "And there's your great-uncle Schuyler.
He was my oldest brother. I guess," he continued, "some of

these people here with us today are the sons and daughters of people who put things in the time capsule. I'm probably the only one old enough to have been around then!"

"How'd you get to put something in the capsule?" I asked him.

"Well, they had a contest in the newspaper. I had to write, in twenty-five words or less, what I'd put in the time capsule if I got the chance, and why."

"And you were one of the winners! What did you say, Grandpa?"

"It was so long ago . . . Well, I think I said, 'I want to put a photo of me and my brother and our mom in the time capsule, so that seventy-six years from now I can bring my beautiful great-granddaughter here and show her how funny . . . I mean nerdy . . . we looked.' "

"Grandpa, did you really say that?"

"Of course," he said.

"No, you didn't! That's more than twenty-five words."

Grandpa just grinned.

When we got home from the city that day, I decided I wanted to bury a time capsule of my own. Grandpa said he would help me. It would be fun deciding what to put in it. How did *I* want to be remembered? What things would show best what it's like to live in the year 1991? How long would it be before someone found it? What would the world be like then?

Mom said it would be O.K. to dig a hole in the yard—as long as I didn't dig up her rosebushes.

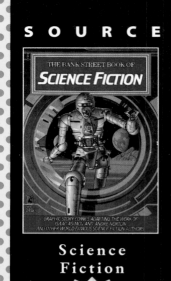

from
The Bank Street Book of Science Fiction

THE FUN THEY HAD

BY ISAAC ASIMOV

Adapted by Dwight Jon Zimmerman
Illustrated by Evan Dorkin

THE SOLAR STUDIES SECTION WAS JUST GEARED TOO FAST FOR HER, SO I HAVE REPROGRAMMED IT TO THE PROPER LEVEL.

ACTUALLY, MARGIE, YOUR OVERALL PROGRESS IS QUITE SATISFACTORY.

OH DIARY, WHAT I REALLY WANTED WAS FOR THE INSPECTOR TO TAKE MY TEACHER AWAY! BUT, BACK TO TOMMY'S BOOK....

YOU STILL HAVEN'T TOLD ME *WHY* ANYONE WOULD WANT TO WRITE ABOUT SCHOOL.

BECAUSE IT WASN'T *OUR* KIND OF SCHOOL, STUPID.

SCHOOL TIME

Kids Predict the Future

SOURCE

SCHOLASTIC NEWS

News
Magazine

Scholastic News asked third graders around the country what they think the future will be like. Here is what some of them said.

There will be no school. We will learn from computers and robots at home.

**Megan Brock
The Dalles, Oregon**

Robots might do jobs that are dangerous for people and jobs like washing dishes. They could also become our friends.

**Casey Allison
Baraboo, Wisconsin**

Houses will have inflatable floats under them for any water emergency such as a flood or a hurricane.

**Cedric Mims
Cedar Hill, Texas**

Cars will be solar-powered. In the night they will be battery operated.

**Jamie Sanderson
Slaterville Springs,
New York**

We will visit other planets. We will make friends with people on other planets. Astronauts will have to learn lots of languages to communicate with others.

**Harry Gomez
Fairfax, Virginia**

Looking Ahead

Here is how some children responded to a poll.

		Yes	No
1.	Will kids go to school all year long?	32	68
2.	Will you need a computer to do your job?	62	38
3.	Will we discover life in outer space?	60	40
4.	Will there be a cure for cancer?	88	12
5.	Will cats still be the most popular pet?	22	78

PROJECT

How to
Make a Time Capsule

Create a *time capsule* **that tells** kids in the *future* about *life* **today.**

Think about this. In the future, people will study us to learn what our lives were like. Someday your neighborhood may be an archaeological site! And someone may even find a time capsule buried there. A time capsule is a container that is filled with objects and information about a certain time and place. It gets stored away to be discovered sometime in the future.

1 Gather Artifacts

What can you put into a time capsule? You can put in anything that tells about your life as a third grader. It might be an empty box from your favorite cereal, a photograph of a popular sports star, a class picture, a magazine ad for a movie you like, or a list of this week's spelling words. You might even write a diary about a day at school.

Things to Put in a Time Capsule
- menus
- jokes
- photographs
- newspapers, magazines, or catalogs
- picture postcards
- recipes for favorite foods
- tapes of favorite songs

TOOLS

- paper and pencil
- index cards
- large waterproof container made of plastic or metal
- artifacts to place into your time capsule
- clear plastic bags
- paper folder

Gather as many artifacts as you can. Now put all your artifacts into one place. Look at them closely. Decide which ones best tell about life today. These will go into your time capsule. Make a list of the artifacts you want to use.

Tips
- Place paper artifacts into clear plastic bags.
- Don't choose foods, plants, or liquids.
- Make sure objects will fit in to the time capsule.

KING STREET SCHOOL
1994 1995
MRS. WARREN
3RD GRADE

2 Label the Artifacts

You can give kids of the future more information about each artifact, too.

- Make a label for each artifact. On an index card, write the name of the artifact, what it is, and why it is important to you.

- Then tape or tie the label to the artifact.

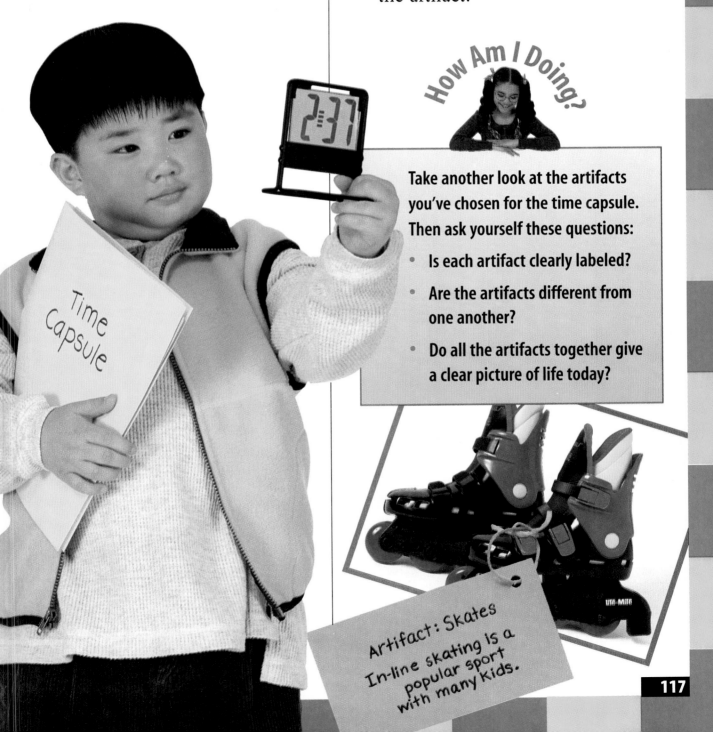

How Am I Doing?

Take another look at the artifacts you've chosen for the time capsule. Then ask yourself these questions:

- Is each artifact clearly labeled?

- Are the artifacts different from one another?

- Do all the artifacts together give a clear picture of life today?

Time Capsule

Artifact: Skates
In-line skating is a popular sport with many kids.

3 | Greet the Future

Think of what you want to say to the kids who will open your time capsule. Write a short letter to them. Tell them about yourself. Describe what life is like today— what you like about it and what you would change.

Share your hopes for the future, too. Make a copy of your letter. Put it into a folder with your artifact list. Now you have a record of all the things you placed in your time capsule.

4 Put the Capsule Together

Share your artifacts with the class, and tell why you chose each one. Then put your time capsule together. Carefully place your artifacts and the letter to the future inside the container you've chosen—a large plastic jar or a metal box with a tight-fitting lid. Close it up. If you like, decorate the outside of the time capsule.

When do you want your time capsule opened? In 10, 20, or even 50 years? Decide on a date in the future.

Find a place to store your time capsule. It might be in the principal's office or in your school library or in your schoolroom. Sometime in the future, another group of third graders will open it and discover what was important to you.

If You Are Using a Computer ...

Create a Journal entry on the computer about a typical day in your classroom. Then print it out to include in your time capsule. You also can write your letter to the future on the computer. Include clip art that tells about your life today.

These artifacts were collected by:

Date: Place:

Do not open until:

CONGRATULATIONS

Now you've become a real time detective. You can find clues to the past all around you. Keep looking for them!

Dr. Ruben Mendoza
Archaeologist ▶

Glossary

an·ces·tor
(an′ses tər) *noun*
A person, now dead, from whom one is descended. One *ancestor* of mine moved to America from Russia in the late 1800s.

an·cient
(ān′shənt) *adjective*
Very old or very long ago. At the museum I saw *ancient* toys that were made thousands of years ago.

Thesaurus

ancient
old
aged
antique

ar·chae·ol·o·gist
(är′kē ol′ə jist) *noun*
A person who studies people or things from a long time ago. The *archaeologist* discovered three mummies from ancient Egypt.

ar·row·heads
(ar′ō hedz′) *noun*
The pointed tips of arrows. Long ago, *arrowheads* were made of sharpened stones.
▲ **arrowhead**

ar·ti·fact
(är′tə fact′) *noun*
A tool or object made and used by people a long time ago. The archaeologist found an *artifact* that looked like a clay marble.

chim·ney
(chim′nē) *noun*
A hollow structure in a building—often made of bricks or stones—that carries away smoke from a fireplace or furnace.

chimney

clues (kloos) *noun*
Hints that help solve a problem, a mystery, or a puzzle. The footprints are *clues* that someone had walked through the yard.
▲ **clue**

com•put•er
(kəm pyoo'tər) *noun*
An electronic machine
that can store information
and solve complicated
problems quickly.

Fact File

The first modern
machine for computing
was invented in 1946. It
weighed 30 tons, and
performed 100,000
operations per second.

---

e•lec•tron•ic
(i lek tron'ik) *adjective*
Having to do with
equipment such as
radios, televisions,
and computers.

foun•da•tion
(foun dā'shən) *noun*
The bottom or base of a
building, usually below
ground. The workers
built the new house on
top of a stone *foundation*.

grid (grid) *noun*
A set of straight lines
that cross to form
squares. We drew a *grid*
over our town map so
that we could find our
friends' houses.

horse•shoe
(hôrs'shoo') *noun*
A flat, U-shaped metal
plate. It is nailed to the
bottom of a horse's hoof
to protect it.

jour•nals
(jûr'nlz) *noun*
Diaries or records of
what happens each day.
▲ **journal**

leg•end (lej'ənd) *noun*
A story that is handed
down through the years.
Some or all of the story
may not be true.

Word Study

The phrase "a **legend**
in his own time," refers to
a person whose accomplish-
ments are so great that
they will be recorded in
history books.

---

a	add	oo	took	ə =		
ā	ace	oo	pool	ə in *above*		
â	care	u	up	e in *sicken*		
ä	palm	û	burn	i in *possible*		
e	end	yoo	fuse	o in *melon*		
ē	equal	oi	oil	u in *circus*		
i	it	ou	pout			
ī	ice	ng	ring			
o	odd	th	thin			
ō	open	th	this			
ô	order	zh	vision			

Glossary

mam•moth
(mam′əth) *noun*
A large animal, like an elephant, that lived long ago. It had shaggy brown hair and long curved tusks.

man•sion
(man′shən) *noun*
A very large and elegant home. The *mansion* had 30 rooms and a long driveway.

pet•ro•glyphs
(pe′trə glifs′) *noun*
Carvings or drawings on a rock. ▲ **petroglyph**

phot•o•graphs
(fo′tə grafs′) *noun*
Pictures taken with a camera. ▲ **photograph**

pueb•lo
(pweb′lō) *noun*
A Native American village that is made up of stone or adobe buildings built one above the other. Pueblos are found in the southwestern United States.

Word History

Pueblo comes from a Spanish word meaning "people" or "town." Long ago, Spanish explorers thought that Native American adobe villages in the Southwest looked like towns in Spain. The Native Americans who live in these adobe villages are also known as **Pueblo** Indians.

pyr•a•mid
(pir′ə mid) *noun*
A solid object with a flat base and triangular sides that meet at a point at the top. Some structures are built in the shape of a pyramid.

quilt (kwilt) *noun*
A bed cover made of two layers of colorful cloth with a layer of feathers or soft material between them. The stitches used to sew a *quilt* make patterns on the cloth.

re•cord (ri kôrd′) *verb*
To write down for future use. The teacher will *record* the students' test scores.

re•mem•ber
(ri mem′bər) *verb*
To bring back to mind. I *remember* my trip to Yellowstone Park last summer.

re•pro•grammed
(rē prō′gramd) *verb*
Gave new instructions to a computer about how to do its work. ▲ **reprogram**

petroglyph

re•stor•a•tion
(res´tə rā´shən) *noun*
The act of making
something like new or
like it once was. After its
restoration, the old bicycle
looked brand new.

ru•ins (roo´inz) *noun*
Buildings that have fallen
apart or have been
destroyed. We visited the
ruins of an old castle on
our vacation. ▲ **ruin**

sa•ber-toothed ti•ger
(sā´bər tootht´ tī´gər)
noun
A large animal of the
cat family that lived
long ago. It looked
somewhat like a modern-
day tiger and had long,
sharp upper teeth.

sal•vage (sal´vij) *verb*
To save from loss or
destruction. After the flood
we were able to *salvage*
some of our furniture.

stores (storz) *verb*
Puts away for future use.
My mother *stores* cans of
food in the cupboard.
▲ **store**

stor•y•tel•ler
(stôr´ē tel´ər) *noun*
A person who tells stories
for fun or learning.

sun•di•al
(sun´dī´əl) *noun*
An ancient kind of a
clock. It shows the time
of day by a shadow the
sun makes on a dial.

tribe (trīb) *noun*
A group of people
with the same ancestors,
customs, and language.
The Hopi are a *tribe*
of Native Americans
who live in the
American Southwest.

Thesaurus

tribe
clan
family
kin

tusks (tusks) *noun*
Long, curving teeth.
They stick out of the side
of an animal's mouth.
Elephants and walruses
have tusks. ▲ **tusk**

sundial

a	add	o͞o	took	ə =
ā	ace	o͞o	pool	a in *above*
â	care	u	up	e in *sicken*
ä	palm	û	burn	i in *possible*
e	end	yo͞o	fuse	o in *melon*
ē	equal	oi	oil	u in *circus*
i	it	ou	pout	
ī	ice	ng	ring	
o	odd	th	thin	
ō	open	th	this	
ô	order	zh	vision	

Authors & Illustrators

Aliki *pages 86–95*

Author/illustrator Aliki has loved to draw since she was a very little girl. In fact, her kindergarten teacher predicted she would be an artist someday. Today Aliki does more than draw. She creates books about things that interest her. She says, "Writing and illustrating books is a way of satisfying my curiosity. I'm just lucky that children are curious about the same things I am." Many of Aliki's books, such as *Wild and Woolly Mammoths* and *How a Book Is Made,* are nonfiction. She enjoys doing research and tries to make facts easy to understand. Aliki has written more than 40 books since she began her career in 1961.

Isaac Asimov *pages 104–112*

When he was just 17, Isaac Asimov sent his first science fiction story to a magazine. It was rejected! But he didn't give up and sent in another a few months later. It was accepted. Mr. Asimov went on to become a very successful science fiction writer. He wrote nonfiction books about science topics. In all, he wrote nearly 500 books! The author, who died in 1992, often wrote 18 hours a day, 7 days a week.

Gail Gibbons *pages 32–51*

This award-winning author/illustrator writes nonfiction books about the different things that interest and excite her—from how mail moves to how clocks work. She spends a lot of time doing research. Often she finds far more information than she can use. She then narrows down the facts to those that are the most fun and important. She suggests that young writers pick subjects that they know and like. That way they will enjoy writing a lot more.

Patricia and Fredrick McKissack

pages 58–71

This award-winning team wants to bring the past alive for young readers. Many of their books tell about African Americans who have made important contributions to the world. The McKissacks work well together. Fredrick McKissack does most of the research, while Patricia McKissack does most of the writing. Then, together, they rewrite until each book is just the way they want it.

"The people of the past have a great deal to teach us. We can learn from their tragedies and triumphs."

Jerry Pinkney *pages 10–23*

After he reads a manuscript for a book he is going to illustrate, Jerry Pinkney imagines what the characters look like. He does historical research about the subject, if he needs to. Pinkney also uses real people as models to help him develop the characters. He even keeps a closet full of interesting clothes for the models to wear. He lets them read the story and act it out! This way, Pinkney captures the right body movements and expressions for the characters in his drawings.

Books &

Author/Illustrator Study

More by Patricia and Fredrick McKissack

Carter G. Woodson: The Father of Black History
This biography tells the story of a man who wanted everyone to discover the achievements of African Americans.

Christmas in the Big House, Christmas in the Quarters
This book brings to life a holiday celebration from the past.

Flossie and the Fox
What happens when a little girl meets a fox in the woods? In her version of this old folk tale, Patricia McKissack creates two very memorable characters.

Fiction

Chang and the Paper Pony
by Eleanor Coerr
illustrated by Deborah Ray
In this story, set in the time of the California gold rush, a boy named Chang dreams of owning a pony of his own.

The Courage of Sarah Noble
by Alice Dalgliesh
Sarah is a pioneer and proud of it! She does what she can to help her family when they move west.

The Sunday Outing
by Gloria Pinkney
illustrated by Jerry Pinkney
Ernestine enjoys visiting with her great-grandmother in North Carolina and learning about all the things her parents and grandparents did long ago.

Nonfiction

Corn Is Maize
by Aliki
Did you know that people have been growing corn for thousands of years? This book tells how scientists have studied corn to learn about life in America long ago.

The Seminoles: A First American's Book
by Virginia Driving Hawk Sneve
illustrated by Ronald Himler
This book traces the history of the Seminole people and also tells how they live today.

&Media

Videos

Follow The Drinking Gourd
Rabbit Ears
This animated tale tells how one brave family escaped from slavery. (30 minutes)

Paul Bunyan
SVS/Rabbit Ears
Meet a tall-tale hero from America's past! In this version of the classic story, the mighty logger ends up feeling sorry that he cut down so many trees—so he finds a way to make the forests green again. (30 minutes)

Software

20th Century Video Almanac Overview
Software Toolworks (IBM/CD-ROM)
This amazing reference source uses videos, photos, and sound to show you important events from the past hundred years.

Where in Time Is Carmen Sandiego?
Broderbund (Apple, Macintosh, IBM)
Carmen and her gang zoom through history in a time machine. Where are they headed? What are they planning? It's up to you to stop them!

Magazines

Children's Album
What items would you place in a time capsule to tell about life today? This magazine may help you think of ideas. It's full of artwork and writing by children as well as step-by-step instructions for lots of craft projects.

National Geographic World
This magazine allows you to travel around the world without leaving your chair. Read about archaeological discoveries, outdoor adventures, and more!

A Place to Write

Junior Philatelists of America
Post Office Box 1600
Trenton, NJ 08607

Stamps can tell you about a country's history. This club is for kids who are interested in stamp collecting. Write for information and the club newsletter. Include a self-addressed stamped envelope.

Community
Quilt

New Harvest $1.39
NET WT. 1g
ALASKA
SHASTA DAISY

New Harvest $1.39
NET WT. 1g
SWISS GIANT MIXED COLORS
PANSY

Visit
a Community Garden

In a community, some things continue and some things change.

That's the Spirit!

A community improves through the contributions of individuals.

Interested in joining...
Linden Heights
Neighborhood
Garden?
Find out how...
Come to a garden

New Horizons

A community grows through the contributions of newcomers.

YOU MIGHT MAKE
A FRIEND ALONG
THE WAY

Family Biscuits

2 cups all-purpose flour
1 tablespoon baking powder
1 teaspoon salt
1/3 cup shortening
3/4 cup milk

1. Heat oven to 425°F.

Keepsakes

A community is strengthened by preserving landmarks and traditions.

Trade Books

The following books accompany this *Community Quilt* SourceBook.

City Green

by DyAnne DiSalvo-Ryan

Cloudy With a Chance of Meatballs

by Judi Barrett illustrated by Ron Barrett

Lily and Miss Liberty

by Carla Stevens illustrated by Deborah Kogan Ray

Samuel's Choice

by Richard Berleth illustrated by James Watling

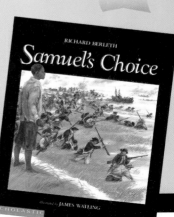

A community improves through the contributions of individuals.

That's the Spirit!

Join Peter Stuyvesant as he cleans up old New York. Then discover how present-day Pittsburgh fought pollution—and won.

Find out how a dream helps a litterbug change his ways.

Dig into Dayton, Ohio's community gardens with Lorka Muñoz.

WORKSHOP 1

Create a public-service poster for your community.

Interested in joining...
Linden Heights Neighborhood Garden?
Find out how...
Come to a garden planning meeting
Thursday, July 6
St. Anthony School Cafeteria

9

On The Day Peter Stuyvesant Sailed Into Town

by ARNOLD LOBEL

On the day Peter Stuyvesant sailed into town
All the people came running to greet him.
They shot off a cannon and waited in line
So that every last Dutchman could meet him.

"My friends," Peter said, "it is nice to be here
For my voyage was really a long one.
I will rule this new land with a very firm hand,
And my government will be a strong one.
Yes, my government will be a strong one."

Peter Stuyvesant stood with a leg made of wood,
And he said, "There is no time to talk now.
It's a very fine day, this eleventh of May,
So I think I will go for a walk now."

And into New Amsterdam Peter did go
To see all there was to be seen.
But he soon wore a frown as he walked up and down—
He discovered that nothing was clean.

The governor slipped in the mud and the mire,
And he said, "Things are not at all well here.
I am standing in garbage right up to my knees,
And the air has a very bad smell here.
Yes, the air has a very bad smell here."

"All the houses in town are in need of repair,"
Peter shouted. "I loudly decry it!
This whole dirty place is a total disgrace.
Good Dutchmen, we must beautify it!"

But the folk of the town went on smoking their pipes,
And they said, "It is best to ignore him.
There will soon come a day he will be on his way
Like the men who have governed before him."

From Broadway to Wall Street old Stuyvesant stormed;
With a tap and a step he kept walking,
While some chickens and ducks made a nest in his hat
And some geese on the path made a squawking.
Yes, those geese on the path made a squawking.

Then a goat from behind, in a manner unkind,
Gave Peter a push on his seat.
A cow licked his nose and some pigs chewed his toes
As poor Stuyvesant sat in the street.

"This New World is a mess!" Peter cried in distress.
"These animals need gates and fences.
Take these birds to a cage!" Peter shouted in rage.
"Oh, good Dutchmen, let's come to our senses!"

As his voice rocked the ground with a great, booming sound,
Like a sky filled with thunder and lightning,
Those good Dutchmen did shake—they cried, "Make no mistake,
This man's temper is really quite frightening!"

While the citizens stood in a trembling group
Peter cried, "Here is my proclamation.
All you men and you maids, get your brooms and your spades.
We must work now without hesitation!
Yes, let's work now without hesitation!"

So they put up new buildings all sturdy and strong,
And they cleaned all the rubbish away.
They mended the fences and paved many streets
From the top of the town to the bay.

They filled up the holes in the walls of the fort,
For the colony needed protection.
And the people agreed they were clever to heed
Peter Stuyvesant's careful direction.

Some ten or twelve summers had come and had gone
As they worked on the east and the west side.
Things were going so well it was soon hard to tell
Which half of that town was the best side.

"My children," said Peter, "we've worked very hard,
And I think we deserve relaxation.
I feel in the mood for some fun and some food.
Let us have a big Dutch celebration!
Yes, it's time for a big celebration!"

Each New Amsterdam nose sniffed the smells that arose
In delicious fat clouds to the air.
How they gave such delight to each Dutch appetite,
All those good things to eat everywhere.

Someone asked, "Will this town stay as small as it is?"
Well, of course, there was no way of knowing,
So they danced until evening all dizzy and gay
And went home as the darkness was growing.

That night Peter Stuyvesant heard a strange sound
Underneath a round moon brightly gleaming.
It swept past his door, a great tumble and roar,
But old Stuyvesant knew he was dreaming . . .

Yes, Peter Stuyvesant knew he was dreaming.

S O U R C E

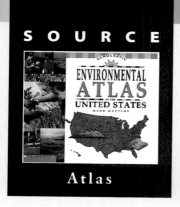

Atlas

from
Scholastic Environmental Atlas
of the United States

How Pittsburgh

by Mark Mattson

Here is what Pittsburgh looked like when its steel mills were thriving, and how it looks today. Industry in the cities around the Great Lakes—especially steel-works—had declined so much by the 1980s that the area was often described as the Rust Belt.

Cleaned Up

Pittsburgh became an industrial, steel-making giant about 100 years ago. Three major rivers—the Monongahela, the Ohio, and the Allegheny—meet in this western Pennsylvania city. These rivers were used to move iron ore and coal into Pittsburgh's furnaces, and to move finished steel out.

Eventually, the rivers became polluted and started flooding. Belching smokestacks dirtied the air. Huge heaps of slag, the waste from making steel, blemished the earth.

First Clean-up. In the 1950s, industrialists and political leaders joined together to clean up the city. They passed anti-smoke laws to clean up the air. They created locks and dams to tame the rivers. They replaced industrial slums with parks, plazas, and modern buildings.

By the 1970s, Pittsburgh's steel factories were outdated, and the steel industry was failing. As jobs were lost, neighborhoods crumbled.

Good Place to Live. City leaders again joined together to bring in clean industries that use technologies such as biomedicine, robotics, and software to create new jobs. In 1985, Pittsburgh was named America's most livable city. Today, people can even fish in the Monongahela.

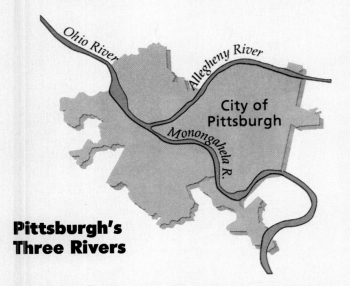

Pittsburgh's Three Rivers

AWARD
WINNING

Book

JUST A DREAM
BY CHRIS VAN ALLSBURG

As usual, Walter stopped at the bakery on his way home from school. He bought one large jelly-filled doughnut. He took the pastry from its bag, eating quickly as he walked along. He licked the red jelly from his fingers. Then he crumpled up the empty bag and threw it at a fire hydrant.

At home Walter saw Rose, the little girl next door, watering a tree that had just been planted. "It's my birthday present," she said proudly. Walter couldn't understand why anyone would want a tree for a present. His own birthday was just a few days away, "And I'm not getting some dumb plant," he told Rose.

After dinner Walter took out the trash. Three cans stood next to the garage. One was for bottles, one for cans, and one for everything else. As usual, Walter dumped everything into one can. He was too busy to sort through garbage, especially when there was something good on television.

The show that Walter was so eager to watch was about a boy who lived in the future. The boy flew around in a tiny airplane that he parked on the roof of his house. He had a robot and a small machine that could make any kind of food with the push of a button.

Walter went to bed wishing he lived in the future. He couldn't wait to have his own tiny plane, a robot to take out the trash, and a machine that could make jelly doughnuts by the thousands. When he fell asleep, his wish came true. That night Walter's bed traveled to . . .

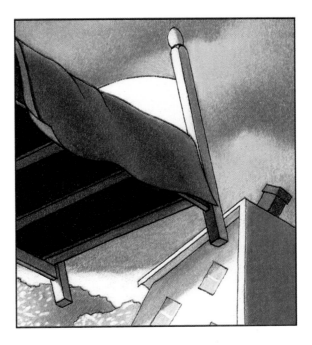

the future.

Walter woke up in the middle of a huge dump. A bulldozer was pushing a heap of bulging trash bags toward him. "Stop!" he yelled.

The man driving the bulldozer put his machine in neutral. "Oh, sorry," he said. "Didn't see you."

Walter looked at the distant mountains of trash and saw half-buried houses. "Do people live here?" he asked.

"Not anymore," answered the man.

A few feet from the bed was a rusty old street sign that read FLORAL AVENUE. "Oh no," gasped Walter. He lived on Floral Avenue.

The driver revved up his bulldozer. "Well," he shouted, "back to work!"

Walter pulled the covers over his head. This can't be the future, he thought. I'm sure it's just a dream. He went back to sleep.

But not for long . . .

Walter peered over the edge of his bed, which was caught in the branches of a tall tree. Down below, he could see two men carrying a large saw. "Hello!" Walter yelled out.

"Hello to you!" they shouted back.

"You aren't going to cut down this tree, are you?" Walter asked.

But the woodcutters didn't answer. They took off their jackets, rolled up their sleeves, and got to work. Back and forth they pushed the saw, slicing through the trunk of Walter's tree. "You must need this tree for something important," Walter called down.

"Oh yes," they said, "very important." Then Walter noticed lettering on the woodcutters' jackets. He could just make out the words: QUALITY TOOTHPICK COMPANY. Walter sighed and slid back under the blankets.

Until . . .

Walter couldn't stop coughing. His bed was balanced on the rim of a giant smokestack. The air was filled with smoke that burned his throat and made his eyes itch. All around him, dozens of smokestacks belched thick clouds of hot, foul smoke. A workman climbed one of the stacks.

"What is this place?" Walter called out.

"This is the Maximum Strength Medicine Factory," the man answered.

"Gosh," said Walter, looking at all the smoke, "what kind of medicine do they make here?"

"Wonderful medicine," the workman replied, "for burning throats and itchy eyes."

Walter started coughing again.

"I can get you some," the man offered.

"No thanks," said Walter. He buried his head in his pillow and, when his coughing stopped, fell asleep.

But then . . .

Snowflakes fell on Walter. He was high in the mountains.
A group of people wearing snowshoes and long fur coats
hiked past his bed.

"Where are you going?" Walter asked.

"To the hotel," one of them replied.

Walter turned around and saw an enormous building.
A sign on it read HOTEL EVEREST. "Is that hotel," asked
Walter, "on the top of Mount Everest?"

"Yes," said one of the hikers. "Isn't it beautiful?"

"Well," Walter began. But the group didn't wait for
his answer. They waved goodbye and marched away.
Walter stared at the flashing yellow sign, then crawled
back beneath his sheets.

But there was more to see . . .

Walter's hand was wet and cold. When he opened his eyes, he found himself floating on the open sea, drifting toward a fishing boat. The men on the boat were laughing and dancing.

"Ship ahoy!" Walter shouted.

The fishermen waved to him.

"What's the celebration for?" he asked.

"We've just caught a fish," one of them yelled back. "Our second one this week!" They held up their small fish for Walter to see.

"Aren't you supposed to throw the little ones back?" Walter asked.

But the fishermen didn't hear him. They were busy singing and dancing.

Walter turned away. Soon the rocking of the bed put him to sleep.

But only for a moment . . .

A loud, shrieking horn nearly lifted Walter off his mattress. He jumped up. There were cars and trucks all around him, horns honking loudly, creeping along inch by inch. Every driver had a car phone in one hand and a big cup of coffee in the other. When the traffic stopped completely, the honking grew even louder. Walter could not get back to sleep.

Hours passed, and he wondered if he'd be stuck on this highway forever. He pulled his pillow tightly around his head. This can't be the future, he thought. Where are the tiny airplanes, the robots? The honking continued into the night, until finally, one by one, the cars became quiet as their drivers, and Walter, went to sleep.

But his bed traveled on . . .

Walter looked up. A horse stood right over his bed, staring directly at him. In the saddle was a woman wearing cowboy clothes. "My horse likes you," she said.

"Good," replied Walter, who wondered where he'd ended up this time. All he could see was a dull yellow haze.

"Son," the woman told him, spreading her arms in front of her, "this is the mighty Grand Canyon."

Walter gazed into the foggy distance.

"Of course," she went on, "with all this smog, nobody's gotten a good look at it for years." The woman offered to sell Walter some postcards that showed the canyon in the old days. "They're real pretty," she said.

But he couldn't look. It's just a dream, he told himself. I know I'll wake up soon, back in my room.

But he didn't . . .

Walter looked out from under his sheets. His bed was flying through the night sky. A flock of ducks passed overhead. One of them landed on the bed, and to Walter's surprise, he began to speak. "I hope you don't mind," the bird said, "if I take a short rest here." The ducks had been flying for days, looking for the pond where they had always stopped to eat.

"I'm sure it's down there somewhere," Walter said, though he suspected something awful might have happened. After a while the duck waddled to the edge of the bed, took a deep breath, and flew off. "Good luck," Walter called to him. Then he pulled the blanket over his head. "It's just a dream," he whispered, and wondered if it would ever end.

Then finally . . .

Walter's bed returned to the present. He was safe in his
room again, but he felt terrible. The future he'd seen was
not what he'd expected. Robots and little airplanes didn't
seem very important now. He looked out his window at
the trees and lawns in the early morning light, then
jumped out of bed.

He ran outside and down the block, still in his pajamas. He found the empty jelly doughnut bag he'd thrown at the fire hydrant the day before. Then Walter went back home and, before the sun came up, sorted all the trash by the garage.

A few days later, on Walter's birthday, all his friends came over for cake and ice cream. They loved his new toys: the laser gun set, electric yo-yo, and inflatable dinosaurs. "My best present," Walter told them, "is outside." Then he showed them the gift that he'd picked out that morning—a tree.

After the party, Walter and his dad planted the birthday present. When he went to bed, Walter looked out his window. He could see his tree and the tree Rose had planted on her birthday. He liked the way they looked, side by side. Then he went to sleep, but not for long, because that night Walter's bed took him away again.

When Walter woke up, his bed was standing in the shade of two tall trees. The sky was blue. Laundry hanging from a clothesline flapped in the breeze. A man pushed an old motorless lawnmower. This isn't the future, Walter thought. It's the past.

"Good morning," the man said. "You've found a nice place to sleep."

"Yes, I have," Walter agreed. There was something very peaceful about the huge trees next to his bed.

The man looked up at the rustling leaves. "My great-grandmother planted one of these trees," he said, "when she was a little girl."

Walter looked up at the leaves too, and realized where his bed had taken him. This was the future, after all, a different kind of future. There were still no robots or tiny airplanes. There weren't even any clothes dryers or gas-powered lawn mowers. Walter lay back and smiled. "I like it here," he told the man, then drifted off to sleep in the shade of the two giant trees—the trees he and Rose had planted so many years ago.

Lorka Muñoz

Grow With Us
Community Garden

·KIDS' PLOTS AVAILABLE·

A GROW WITH YOUR NEIGHBOR'S GARDEN
of the Wegerzyn Horticultural Center
with the Support of the
City of Dayton's
Department of Planning

Community Garden Director

Learn why *community gardens* are here to stay.

Take an empty city lot filled with rusty cans, plastic bottles, and weeds. Add a group of hard-working people, some flower and vegetable seeds, and a few trees. What do you have? "A community garden," says Lorka Muñoz with a big smile.

PROFILE

Name: Lorka Muñoz

Job: community garden director

Born: New York City

What *lorka* means: "Flower" in Russian. With a different spelling, it is also the last name of a famous Spanish poet.

Hobby: fixing up old houses

Most unusual garden you have seen: A kids' garden in Denver, Colorado. The kids used junk to make scarecrows.

Community projects you did as a kid: planting trees

ALL ABOUT
Lorka Muñoz

Here's what Lorka Muñoz *has to say about* **starting a community garden.**

Lorka Muñoz works for an organization in Dayton, Ohio, called Grow With Your Neighbors (GWYN). She helps people all over the city turn empty lots into neighborhood green spots.

"A community garden usually starts with one or two people who have found a place for a garden," says Muñoz. "The first thing I do is meet with them and describe how GWYN can help. Then they start organizing other people in their neighborhood."

Lorka Muñoz has found that all kinds of people join Dayton's community gardens—young children, teenagers, parents, and grandparents. They all have one thing in common. They want to make their neighborhoods better places to live.

Getting a gardening group together and finding an empty lot are the first steps in creating a community garden. Then the fun begins. "The people at GWYN and the gardeners design the garden," says Muñoz.

Each garden has two parts. One is a community space—an area that everyone can use. Muñoz

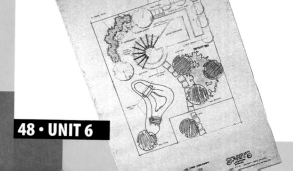

helps the gardeners choose trees and ground covers to plant there. The rest of the garden is divided into small plots where each gardener can plant flowers and vegetables.

Before the planting can begin, the gardeners work together to clean up the lot. They haul away trash, dig up rocks, pull weeds, and prepare the soil. What a job! Then Muñoz helps them get the seeds, plants, and garden tools they need.

By the middle of the summer, the gardeners pick bouquets of flowers and harvest armloads of tasty vegetables. And they share their crops, too. "Some people grow more food than they can eat, so they give away the extra," says Muñoz.

Lorka Muñoz believes that community gardens help neighborhoods in many

ways. "People grow their own fresh food," she says. "Neighbors meet each other and begin to work together. And best of all, the neighborhood looks better."

Lorka Muñoz's
Tips for Improving Your Community

1 Decide exactly what you want to improve.

2 Share your idea with other interested people.

3 Ask for help. Parents or other adults may be willing to lend a hand.

4 Get started. Make a plan, and then carry it out.

How to
Make a Public-Service Poster

community group's project

Communities are always trying to improve themselves. Some have cleanup days. Others plant community gardens. How do communities advertise projects or events like these? One way is to make public-service posters.

What is a public-service poster? A public-service poster is a large printed sign. It has information about a public concern or event. It may be colorfully illustrated.

Interested in joining…

Linden Heights Neighborhood Garden?

Find out how…

Come to a garden planning meeting
Thursday, July 6
St. Anthony School Cafeteria
6:30 - 7:00 p.m.

Sponsored by:
Grow With Your Neighbors
of Wegerzyn Horticultural Center
S.E. Priority Board
Linden Heights Community Council
City of Dayton, Dept. of Planning

the event that is being advertised

place

time

organization that made the poster

colorful decorations

1 Choose an Event

Form a group with several classmates. Decide on an event that will help your community. The event can be a real one that happens in your school or town. It can also be an event that you would like to see happen.

Here are different community events.

- festivals
- cleanup campaigns
- bake sales
- canned-food drives

TOOLS

- paper and pencil
- posterboard
- marking pens, paints, or colored pencils

2 Design the Poster

Your group has chosen an event to announce. Now you can design your poster.

- Decide what you want the poster to say.

- Figure out how it will look. What pictures do you want to go with the words?

- What colors do you want to use?

On a sheet of paper, make a sketch of your design. Do you have all the information you need? Do you like the way it looks?

3 Make a Poster

Now you can make your public-service poster. Decide who will write the words and who will draw the pictures. Remember, neatness counts! When you have finished, take a close look. Are all the words spelled correctly? Have you included the time and place?

FLOWER SALE

May 15
10:00–12:00

Help
Edison School
Buy Computers

Tip A public-service poster may tell community members what they need to bring to an event.

4 Show and Tell

Display your poster in your classroom. Answer any questions your classmates have. Look at their posters, too. How many different kinds of events are advertised? Which events do you think are important?

If You Are Using a Computer …

Create your poster on the computer, using borders and clip art. Remember to experiment with font size and style to make your poster look great.

THINK

People do all kinds of things to help their communities. What kinds of things would you like to do?

Lorka Muñoz
Community Garden Director ▶

A community grows through the contributions of newcomers.

New Horizons

Discover some of the contributions that immigrants have made to our country.

Learn how Mary McLeod Bethune enriched a community in Florida. Find out how some kids honored her for what she did.

WORKSHOP 2

Contribute one of your favorite recipes to a community cookbook.

Family Biscuits

2 cups all-purpose flour
1 tablespoon baking powder
1 teaspoon salt
1/3 cup shortening
3/4 cup milk

1. Heat oven to 425°F.

from

...IF YOUR NAME WAS CHANGED at Ellis Island

by Ellen Levine

illustrated by Wayne Parmenter

From 1892 to 1924, over twelve million immigrants came to the United States from Europe. For most of these newcomers, Ellis Island was the first stop in America. This immigration center was located in New York harbor. Doctors and legal inspectors checked all the immigrants. A few unlucky ones were sent home. But most entered the United States, and many became American citizens.

Why did people come to America?

Many people believed that America was a "Golden Land"—a place where you could get a decent job, go to a free school, and eat well. There was a saying in Polish that people came to America *za chlebem*—"for bread." One person added that they came "for bread, with butter."

In Russia, six-year-old Alec Bodanis was told that in America, "you'll become a millionaire in no time. Take a shovel with you because they shovel gold from the streets." No one knows how these stories began, but Margot Matyshek, age eleven when she left Germany, had also heard that in America, "the streets are paved with gold. And if you wish for candy, it drops from the sky right into your mouth!"

Some people came to look for work. Wages were higher in America than in their home countries. Until the late 1800s, businesses often sent agents overseas to encourage workers to migrate. If you agreed to work for their companies, they would pay your way to America.

Many people came because land was cheap and plentiful. In 1862, the U.S. government passed a law

called the Homestead Act. Newcomers could stake a claim to 160 acres of land. After five years of living on and working the land, they'd pay a small amount of money, and the acres would be theirs. Railroad companies also owned a great deal of land in the west. They sent agents to foreign countries offering this land for sale at good prices.

Some governments of the new western states advertised in European newspapers about their growing towns and cheap farmland. They wanted new settlers. Often the advertisements were not true. They showed pictures of towns that didn't exist, and gave descriptions of farm fields where forests stood. But people came anyway. Searching, always searching, for a better life.

A Swedish song had these words about America:

> "Ducks and chickens rain right down,
> A roasted goose flies in,
> And on the table lands one more
> with knife and fork stuck in."

Who could find a better place?

What did people bring with them?

Usually whatever they could carry. Some had suitcases and trunks. Most had bundles tied together with string. People carried baskets, cardboard boxes, tins, leather sacks—any type of container you could imagine.

They often brought their feather quilts, mattresses, and pillows, for the steamships just provided thin blankets. They packed fancy clothes, specially embroidered and crocheted. Sometimes people wore layers of all their clothing so they wouldn't have to pack them. Often they brought food for the long trip over the ocean, like smoked sausages or hams, or other foods they thought they couldn't get in America.

Many people had to sell or give away almost everything they owned in order to travel to the new land. But sometimes they were able to bring their favorite things. One young girl mailed her dolls to her relatives in America before she herself came. Another brought a book of fairy tales, which she carried in a basket she held tightly for the whole trip.

How long would the ocean trip take?

Until the mid-1800s, most people came to America on sailing ships. These usually took about forty days to cross the Atlantic Ocean, but sometimes it could take up to six months. By the late 1800s, steamships had replaced sailing ships, and the trip was much faster. If there were no bad storms or other problems, the trip usually took anywhere from six to thirty-two days.

Where would you go when you landed at Ellis Island?

When the barge pulled up to the dock at Ellis Island, immigrants walked under the entry arches into the ground-floor baggage room where some left their luggage. Others held on to all their bags. One baggage worker said he could recognize what country people had come from by the type of luggage they carried and by the way they tied the knots around their bundles.

Then they went up a staircase into the Registry Room, also known as the Great Hall. There they would be examined again by doctors and then by immigration inspectors.

As they reached the top of the stairs, the Great Hall spread out before them like a huge maze. Metal pipes divided the space into narrow aisles, and sections were enclosed in wire mesh. One young immigrant said, "You think you're in a zoo!" After 1911, the iron pipes were removed and replaced by long rows of wooden benches.

Hundreds, at times thousands, of immigrants passed through the Great Hall. The noise, some said, was like the Tower of Babel—sometimes thirty languages being spoken at the same time.

Ellis Island was like a miniature city for immigrants. There were waiting rooms, dormitories for over a thousand people, restaurants, a hospital, baggage room, post office, banks to change foreign money, a railroad ticket office, medical and legal examination rooms, baths, laundries, office areas for charities and church groups, and courtrooms.

Ellis Island was the last hurdle you had to pass before you were to enter the country.

What contributions have immigrants made?

From the time of America's founding, new immigrants have played an important role. Eight of the fifty-five men who signed the Declaration of Independence were born in other countries. And when Thomas Jefferson wrote in the Declaration that "all men are created equal," he used the words of his Italian-born friend Philip Mazzei.

History books often list famous Americans who were immigrants. These lists usually include Albert Einstein, the German-Jewish scientist; Alexander Graham Bell, from Scotland, who invented the telephone; Elizabeth Blackwell, English-born, the first woman doctor in America; Knute Rockne, the Norwegian football player and coach; Marcus Garvey, from Jamaica, the leader of the Back-to-Africa movement; Greta Garbo, the Swedish movie star; Spyros Skouras, the Greek movie producer; Irving Berlin, the Russian-Jewish composer and songwriter; Enrico Fermi, the Italian scientist, and many others.

But millions of immigrants, not just the "famous" ones, created or started things that we think of as totally American. We take these things for granted, but they are the contributions of immigrants:

—log cabins first built by Swedes;

—symphony orchestras and glee clubs organized by Germans;

—movies produced in America by Russian Jews and Greeks;

—Santa Claus, bowling, and ice-skating from the Dutch.

Many peoples contributed to American English. "Yankee" is a Dutch word, and "alligator" is Spanish. "Phooey" is from German, and "prairie" is French. "Jukebox" is African, and "gung ho" is Chinese. And there are hundreds more words that were originally foreign and are now part of the English language.

If you think of Native American Indians as the first immigrants, then the names of many states come from Indian "immigrant" languages: Arizona, Wisconsin, Wyoming, Connecticut, Mississippi, and Oklahoma, to name a few. "Raccoon," "skunk," and "succotash" also are Indian words.

As Abraham Lincoln said, immigrants have been "a source of national wealth and strength."

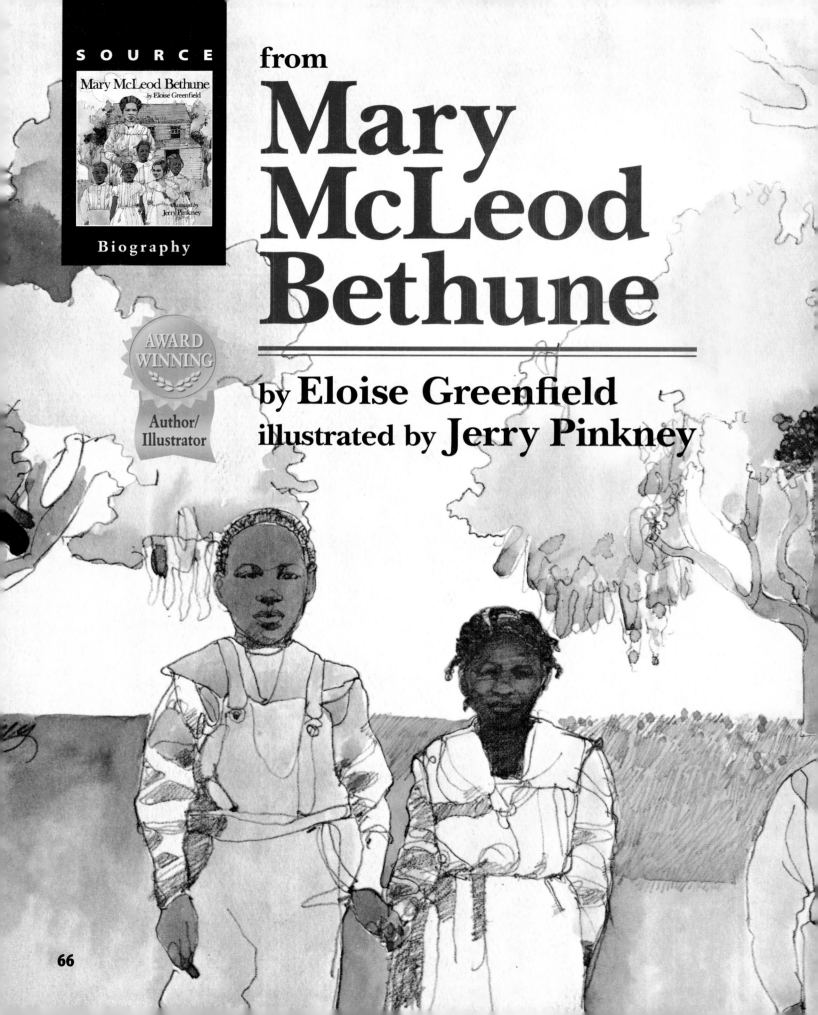

from
Mary McLeod Bethune

by **Eloise Greenfield**
illustrated by **Jerry Pinkney**

As a child, Mary McLeod Bethune dreamed of going to school and learning to read. She finally got her chance in 1886, when she was 11 years old. Emma Wilson and Lucy Laney, both teachers, helped Mary make her dream come true. Once Mary Bethune was on her way, she kept right on going until she became a teacher, too.

A few years after she began teaching, Mary met Albertus Bethune, also a teacher, who became her husband. The following year, their son, Albert, was born.

When Albert was five years old, Mary Bethune made a big decision. She wanted to start a school of her own. She thought of Miss Laney and Miss Wilson, and she remembered herself as a child longing to learn. There were many black children like her who lived in places without schools. They had questions but no answers. They wanted to learn and she wanted to teach them.

She heard about Daytona Beach, Florida, where a new railroad was being built. The workmen who were putting down the railroad track were not being paid enough. They lived with their families in camps that were too crowded. There were no schools. Mrs. Bethune decided that she would go there.

When Mrs. Bethune arrived in Daytona Beach, she had only one dollar and fifty cents. She stayed with a friend, and every day she went for a walk, looking for a building that she could use as a school. Finally, she found an old two-story cottage. The owner said he would rent it to her for eleven dollars a month. He agreed to wait a few weeks until she could raise the first month's rent.

Mrs. Bethune visited the homes of black families, telling them about her school. Neighbors came to paint the cottage and to fix the broken steps. Children helped with the cleaning.

On an autumn day in 1904, Mrs. Bethune stood in the doorway of the cottage, smiling and ringing a bell. It was time for school to start. Five little girls came in and took their seats. The school was named the Daytona Normal and Industrial School for Girls. It was an elementary school, and Albert would learn there, too, until he was older.

Mrs. Bethune and the students used wooden boxes as desks and chairs. They burned logs and used the charcoal as pencils. They mashed berries and used the juice as ink.

The children loved the school. Some of them lived there with Mrs. Bethune. All of them wanted to help raise money for the rent and for the books and paper and lamps and beds that they needed.

After classes, they made ice cream and pies to sell. The children peeled and mashed sweet potatoes while Mrs. Bethune rolled the crust. They gave programs at hotels and in churches. The children sang and recited. Mrs. Bethune spoke to the audiences about the school. She bought a secondhand bicycle and rode all over Daytona Beach, knocking on doors and asking people for their help.

Many people gave. Some of them were rich, and some of them did not have much money themselves but were willing to share the little that they had.

When too many children wanted to attend and a larger building was needed, adults in the community again gave their time and work. They took away the trash from the land that Mrs. Bethune bought. Those who were carpenters helped to put the building up. Those who were gardeners planted flowers and trees around it.

Mrs. Bethune named the new building Faith Hall in honor of her favorite building at Scotia Seminary. She had faith in God, in herself, and in black people. Over the door she hung a sign that said "Enter to learn."

Across from Faith Hall, Mrs. Bethune started a small farm. The students planted fruits and vegetables to use and to sell. They grew strawberries, tomatoes, string beans, carrots, and corn. They grew sugar cane to make syrup.

As the years passed, more students came to the school, and more teachers. More buildings were added. Albert went away to school, but Mrs. Bethune was busier than ever. Almost every day a new problem arose that she had to solve.

One day, a student became very ill. Because there was no hospital for blacks for many, many miles, Mrs. Bethune rushed her to the nearest white hospital. The doctors agreed to take care of her, but not inside the hospital. They put the patient on the back porch with a screen around her bed.

Mrs. Bethune was very angry, but there was nothing she could do. The student was too sick to be moved to another hospital. But when the girl was well, Mrs. Bethune decided that someone had to start a hospital for blacks in Daytona Beach, and she would do it. She started a little two-bed hospital which later had twenty beds. She named it McLeod Hospital in memory of her father, who had died. It saved many black lives.

Later that same year, one of Mrs. Bethune's brothers came for his first visit. He walked around the campus with his sister and visited classrooms where young people were being taught to use their minds and their hands. The choir sang for him. He was proud of his sister and of all that he saw and heard, and Mrs. Bethune was proud to show him what had been done.

Kids Honor

Mary McLeod Bethune

A class in New York City was talking about streets in their neighborhood named after famous African Americans. They discovered several streets that were named after African-American men, such as Martin Luther King, Jr. and Malcolm X.

But there were no streets named after African-American women. The class decided to do something about it.

The students did research about great African-American women and studied maps of the city. Then they voted for a woman and a street. They chose Mary McLeod Bethune because she spent her whole life bringing education to African Americans. In fact, their school is named after her. The class decided to change the name of 134th Street, which runs in front of the building. That way, the students could see the results of their hard work every day. "They can feel a sense of ownership in their community," their teacher said.

The students had to ask their community board and New York's City Council to change the street's name. At a meeting with the City Council, one boy from the class made their case. He said, "We are here today to follow in Mary McLeod Bethune's footsteps. When we learned that there wasn't one street in Harlem named after an African-American woman, we didn't just get mad. We did something about it!"

About a year later, the members of the City Council voted to rename the street. Now New York City has a Mary McLeod Bethune Place, and a class has a lot to be proud of.

class gathers around a sculpture of Mary McLeod Bethune. Thanks to these students, a street has been named after her.

How to
Make a Community Recipe Book

How do people in communities learn about each other? One way is by sharing favorite foods. Some communities even put together community recipe books. The recipe books may contain old recipes, recipes from other countries, or family favorites.

What is a recipe book? A recipe book contains a collection of recipes for foods. A recipe is a list of ingredients and directions for making a food or drink.

YOU MIGHT MAKE A FRIEND ALONG THE WAY

When I was about 7 or 8 years old, I'd come home from school and find my grandmother baking those delicious oversized biscuits. A platter of them would be on top of the stove to keep warm. I'd sneak up to the stove and grab a biscuit then run outside to play. She always caught me, pulled me back by my shirttail and said, "Where are you going?" I'd tell her I was going outside to play. Then she would hand me another biscuit and say, "You'd better take two because you might make a friend along the way."

Phil Mendez
Los Angeles, CA

Family Biscuits

2 cups all-purpose flour
1 tablespoon baking powder
1 teaspoon salt
1/3 cup shortening
3/4 cup milk

1. Heat oven to 425°F.

2. Combine flour, baking powder and salt in large bowl. Mix in shortening until it forms coarse crumbs. Add milk. Mix with fork. Form dough into ball.

3. Put dough on lightly floured surface. Knead gently 8 to 10 times. Roll dough to 1/2-inch thickness. Cut with floured 2-inch round cutter. Place on ungreased baking sheet.

4. Bake at 425°F for 12 to 14 minutes.

Makes 12 to 16 biscuits.

title of recipe tells the kind of food you are making

ingredients you need to make the food

directions for putting the ingredients together

a paragraph that tells why this food is important to you

1 Choose a Recipe

Think of a special food that you like—one that you want to share with your classmates. It might be a recipe that has been in your family for years. You might eat it only on holidays or special occasions. Or it might be a food that your family likes and prepares often. Bring the recipe to class.

TOOLS

• paper and pencil

• colored pencils or marking pens

Here are some different kinds of foods to choose recipes for:

• salads

• breads

• vegetables

• meat or fish dishes

• pasta

• desserts

2 Talk Food

Now you have a recipe. Write a few sentences telling why it is important to you. You may have a happy memory about this food. If it's a holiday food, there may be a story that goes with it. The food may remind you of a special person you know.

3 Write the Recipe

Now you are ready to copy your recipe and your story about it onto a clean sheet of paper. Write down the ingredients and directions carefully. Make sure you have copied everything correctly so that the recipe will come out right. Include your story and write your name at the bottom.

You may wish to decorate your recipe.

Tip Some recipes need special cooking tools. Be sure you include these tools in your recipe's directions.

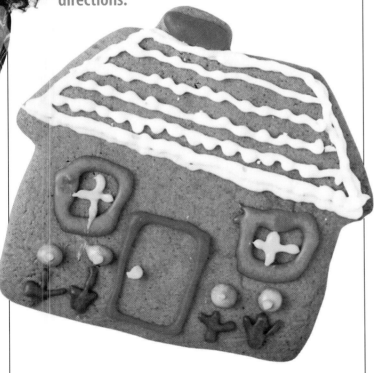

4 It's a Book!

Put all the recipes together to make your community recipe book. Work with your classmates to design a cover. You may want to group similar recipes together. When you have finished, talk about the recipes in your book. Which ones do you know? Which ones are new? Which ones would you like to try?

If You Are Using a Computer ...

Draft your recipe on the computer and decorate it with a special border. You also can create a table of contents for your cookbook on the computer.

THINK

Everyone in a community has different ideas. Why do you think sharing recipes and food is a good way to bring members of a community together?

Lorca Muñoz
*Community
Garden Director* ▶

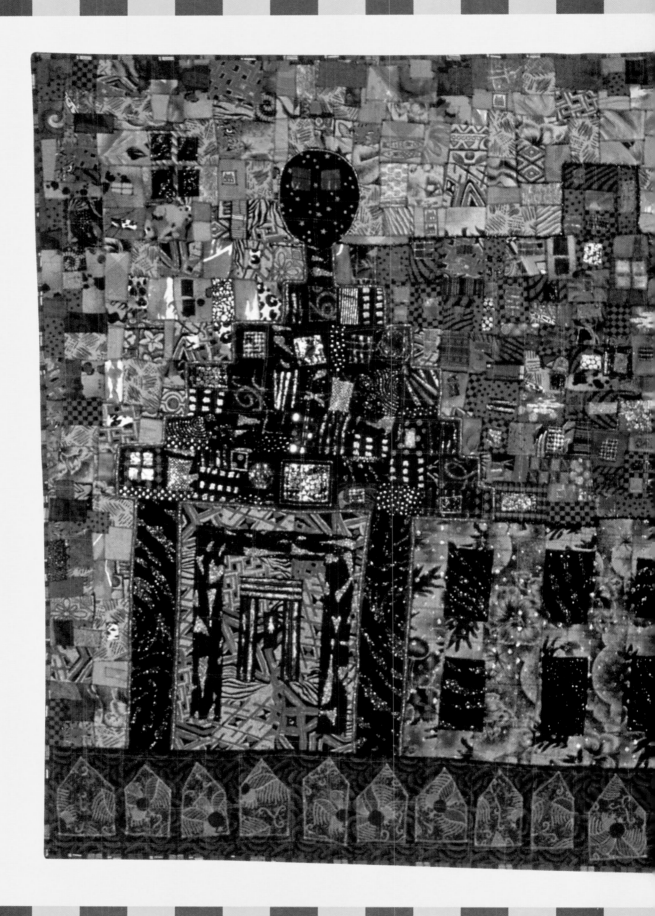

A community is strengthened by preserving landmarks and traditions.

Keepsakes

Watch two friends spring into action to save a special tree. Learn how a group of kids in Massachusetts became heroes of the environment.

Grab your partner and dance to the music of a South American *carnaval.* Chill out at a winter celebration, too.

PROJECT

Design one of the squares in a community quilt.

SQUIRREL PARK

BY LISA CAMPBELL ERNST

To most people in Springdale, Chuck and Stuart were an unlikely pair of best friends.

Sure, they had their differences. But they also had a lot in common. Like climbing trees, collecting leaves, and—most importantly—loving the ancient, gnarled oak tree that grew in the center of town.

For Chuck the magnificent tree was *home*. He grew up in its strong branches, and he played, ate, and slept there.

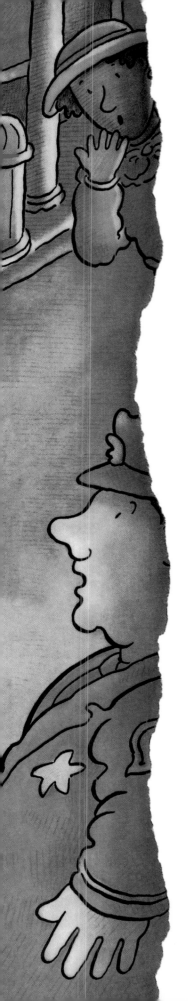

As the town of Springdale grew, its old trees were chopped down one by one, to make room for new buildings. Finally, Chuck's was the last giant to escape the builder's plans.

Even as the other squirrels left town for more trees, Chuck remained loyal. "This tree is my home," he insisted. "Forever."

Stuart loved the tree as well, from the smell of its fresh new buds in spring, to the veiny old bark that told of the tree's long history.

It was Stuart's father—Mr. Ivey—who had built the new buildings in town, and they were just like him: big, straight, and powerful. Stuart was none of those things.

"Out with the old, in with the new!" Mr. Ivey thundered as the trees were cut down to make room for his buildings. "Someday, Stuart, you will follow in my footsteps!" Mr. Ivey told his son.

Stuart shuddered at the thought. "I promise I'll protect your tree," he told Chuck, "no matter what."

Then one morning Stuart's father broke the calm. "STUART!" he roared from the base of the tree.

"Yes, Dad?" Stuart called timidly.

Mr. Ivey frowned. "Son, you know I don't approve of you lollygagging here with that—that *rodent*," he shouted, "but since you insist, I've decided . . . we will build a park here."

Mr. Ivey rushed on. "This is your first job, Stuart. *You* will design the park."

"But how?" Stuart asked.

"Draw a picture," Mr. Ivey instructed, "of how the park should look. You will show your drawing at the town meeting this Saturday. Then the park will be built just that way."

Mr. Ivey turned to leave. "This is an important job, son," he called back. "Don't let me down."

At first Chuck and Stuart just stared at each other in disbelief. "A park!" Stuart shouted at last, and the two friends began to dance around the tree. Chuck leapt and twirled.

"We'll plant a hundred *more* trees!" cried Stuart. "Walnut! Pecan! Chestnut! And we'll make nature paths, and a playground . . ."

Chuck looked up into the mass of swaying, dancing leaves above him. And just for a second, he could have sworn he saw the tree smile.

The next morning, Chuck and Stuart got busy—Saturday's town meeting was two days away. Drawing their plot of land, Stuart filled pages with curving, curling paths, with playgrounds and flowers. Chuck dipped his paws in green ink and marked where each tree would be planted. At the center of it all, they drew their spectacular tree.

"Perfect," Stuart said proudly. And Chuck agreed.

Suddenly, though, Mr. Ivey burst into the room. "I see I'm just in time!" he roared, and thrust a strange-looking box into Stuart's hands.

"For your drawing!" Mr. Ivey shouted, taking out two strange wooden tools and sweeping Chuck and Stuart's artwork off the table.

Mr. Ivey demonstrated how to slide a pencil along the edge of one tool to draw a flat, straight line. With the other tool, he drew straight lines at an angle, and straight lines up and down.

"Beautiful!" Mr. Ivey sang. "*You* will demonstrate these tools at the town meeting. Like father, like son!"

"But—" Stuart began, "I thought curved paths would look nice with the tree." Chuck quickly nodded.

"Nonsense!" Mr. Ivey barked on his way out the door. "With all of my straight buildings in town, I need a park to match."

Stuart stared blankly at Mr. Ivey's drawing and tools. "Now what?" he asked glumly.

Chuck led him back to the tree, in answer.

Unrolling the drawing there, Stuart discovered Mr. Ivey had drawn paths straight through the tree. "We'll have to change that," Stuart gasped, curving the paths around it.

As Chuck chattered his approval, Stuart drew more: playgrounds and curving paths mixed in with Mr. Ivey's straight ones. Soon Chuck got busy with the green ink. And again, at the center of it all, they drew their fabulous tree.

The next morning, Chuck and Stuart bounded into Mr. Ivey's office with their drawing.

"Our park!" Stuart proudly sang. "For tomorrow's town meeting!"

Mr. Ivey frowned at what he saw.

"We used some of the straight lines from your tools," Stuart quickly pointed out, explaining about the path through the tree, "and added our own curved ones—"

"But the tools' lines were *perfect*!" Mr. Ivey interrupted. "Who cares about that old tree?"

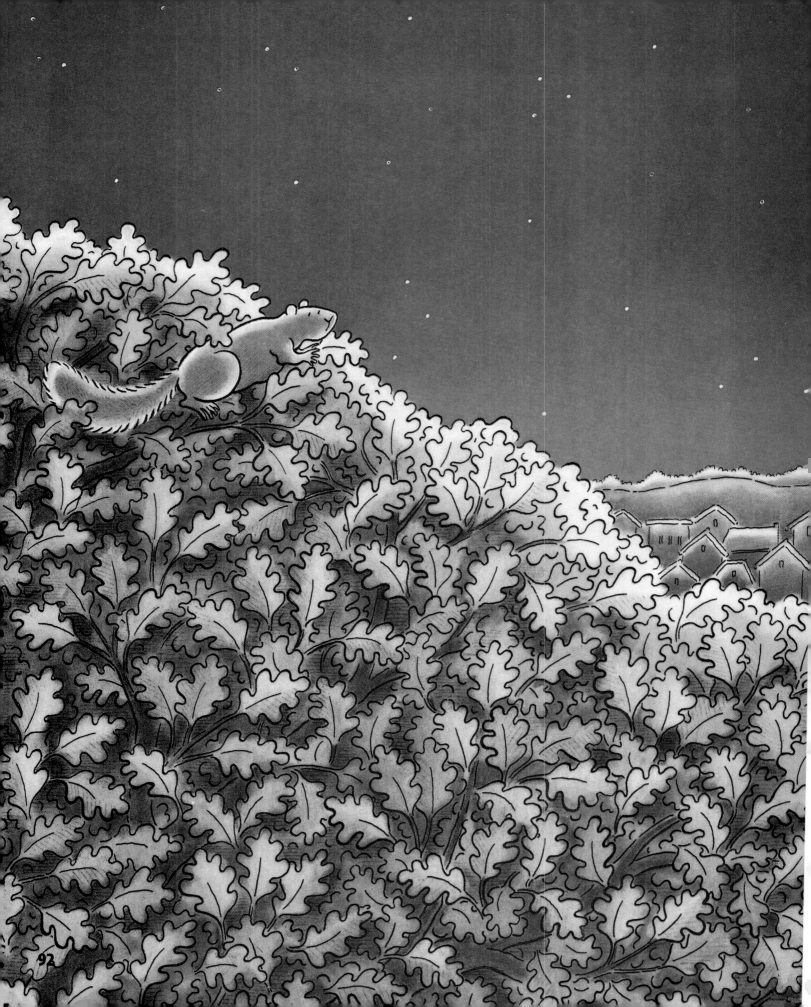

Hearing that, Chuck leapt to his feet. CRASH! Three bottles of ink toppled over.

"Out!" Mr. Ivey shouted as the ink swam across their artwork. "Both of you! I'll do a new drawing myself!"

Stuart's father sent him straight home, so Chuck sat alone, at the top of the tree.

"Don't worry," was the last thing Stuart had said.

But Chuck *was* worried. He could still hear Mr. Ivey's voice asking, "Who cares about that old tree?"

"*I* do!" Chuck now called out. "*I* care!" By nightfall, Chuck was frantic.

Suddenly, Chuck saw Mr. Ivey leave his office, carrying the tools and his new drawing. Disappearing into the town hall, he reappeared moments later, empty-handed.

Chuck now sprang into action.

Racing to the town hall, Chuck squeezed through the mail slot. "That drawing is here somewhere," he said.

And he was right. There in the great hall, it sat with Mr. Ivey's tools and art supplies, ready for the demonstration. Chuck inched past the rows of empty chairs until one giant leap landed him square in the middle of the park drawing.

He quickly surveyed the park at his feet—straight paths, a puny playground, no flowers at all. But it was not until Chuck moved off the center of the drawing that he realized the worst: *His tree was not there.*

Chuck could not believe his eyes. He frantically searched the paper—surely the tree was somewhere. But it was not. His tree was to be cut down.

"Don't panic," Chuck told himself. "*Do* something."

First Chuck rolled up Mr. Ivey's drawing and buried it in the pot of a fern nearby. "That takes care of that," he announced.

But turning around, Chuck eyed the tools and art supplies. "He'll make another one," Chuck realized, "just like it."

"Unless . . ." Chuck said, picking up a wooden tool and smelling it. "Maybe . . ." Suddenly the town hall was filled with a sound that would continue all through the night.

The sound of nibbling.

When Stuart and his father arrived at the town hall the next morning, an excited crowd waited.

Mr. Ivey strode proudly to the front. "Ladies and gentlemen!" he called. "I present . . . your park!" And with that, he turned to reach for his drawing.

Suddenly, the fast-talking Mr. Ivey was speechless. "The—the *tools*," he stammered at last. "My *drawing*!" A paper with Chuck's tree—drawn on with tiny green pawprints—lay there. Mr. Ivey turned white.

As the hushed crowd waited expectantly, Stuart spied Chuck hiding in the potted fern, and understood. "May I have your attention," Stuart timidly called, rushing forward.

All eyes now turned to Stuart.

"My father," he quietly began, "has made many wonderful buildings in Springdale—and now a park. Today he has asked me to demonstrate his new tools, created specially for this important park design."

The townspeople clapped, and Mr. Ivey, still dumbstruck, stood silently by. Sliding his pencil along one tool, Stuart began to draw curving, curling paths around Chuck's tree.

As the drawing grew, Stuart talked—about flowers, playgrounds, and nature paths, of new trees and the hope for more squirrels. Mostly, though, he talked about the amazing, ancient tree that was older than the town itself.

By the time Stuart was finished, the townspeople—and Chuck—had jumped to their feet, cheering.

But all of this time, Mr. Ivey stood by, silently watching, listening.

"Mr. Ivey!" the mayor finally called. "Speak to us of your very unusual, very beautiful design!"

Slowly Mr. Ivey stepped forward, first looking at the smiling towns-people, then at the drawing. He shook his head, he hunched his shoulders, he waved his arms. At last he turned to Stuart. "What can I say?" he whispered. "Only my very unusual son could make such an unusual drawing. But you are right. It *is* beautiful."

The townspeople—and Chuck—cheered again.

The park was, indeed, built just like Chuck and Stuart's design. In fact, it became so loved, that soon towns all across the country wanted parks the same. Stuart and Mr. Ivey were quick to oblige, using Chuck's very special tools.

With the passing years, Stuart and Chuck could still be found sitting happily in their grand old tree. From its branches they watched as the other trees grew, and squirrels arrived to make their homes. At last the park, with its squirrels, became so treasured that the townspeople affectionately named it Squirrel Park.

SOURCE

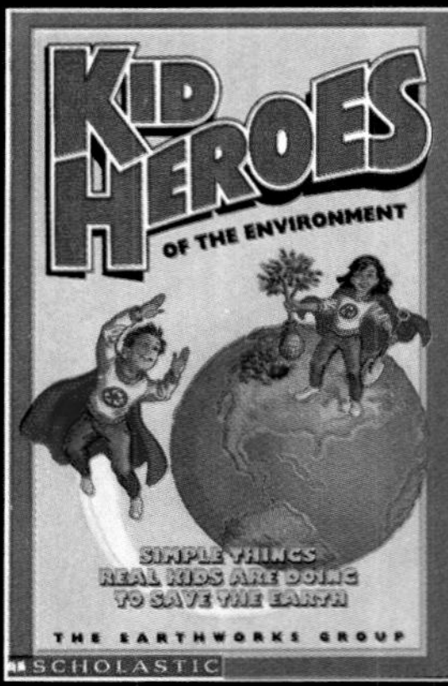

Environmental Handbook

from **KID HEROES OF THE ENVIRONMENT**

PROTECTING

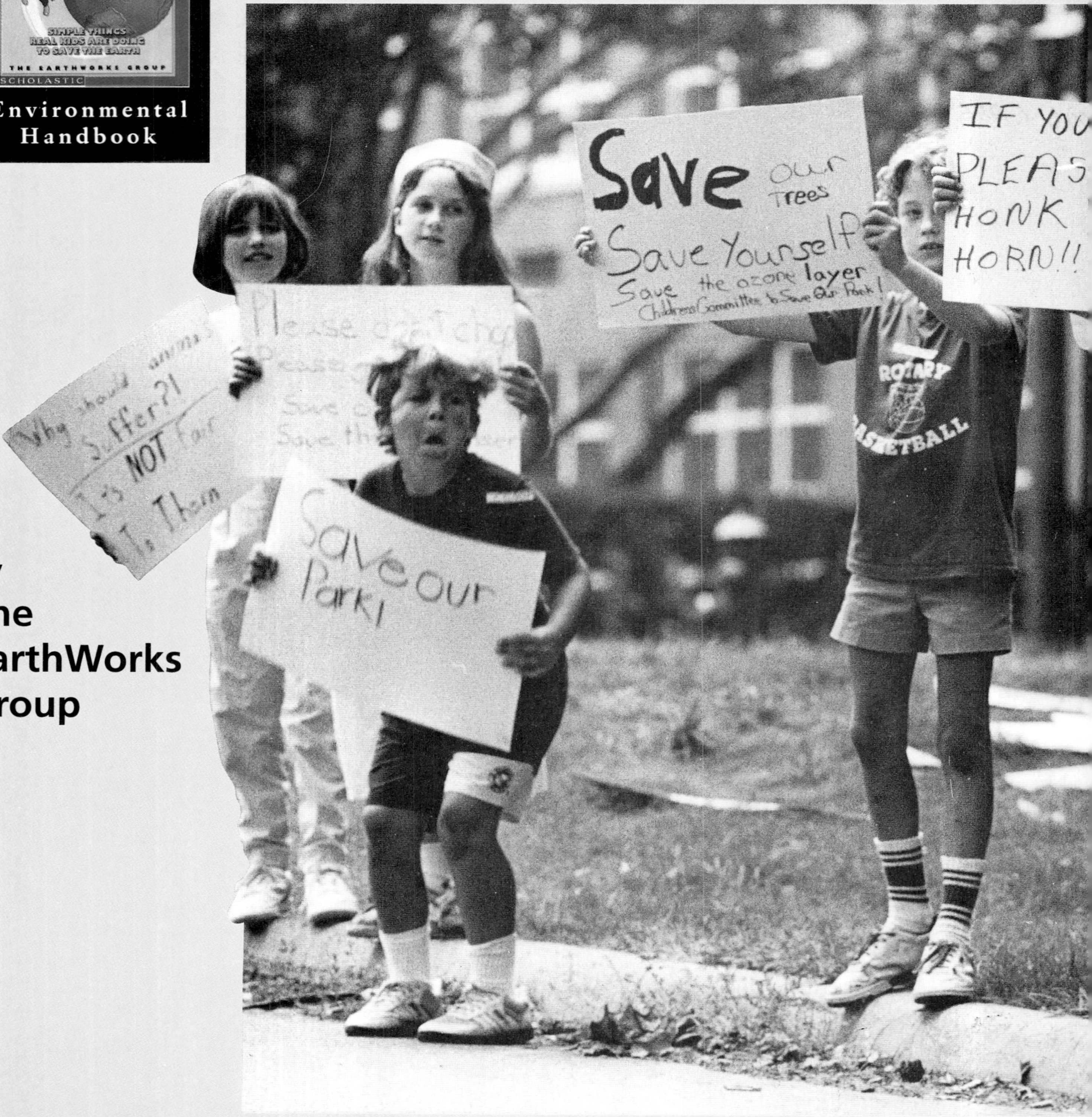

by
The EarthWorks Group

A PARK

KID HEROES

Names: Kate Crowther, Sarah Crowther, Laura Sheppard-Brick, Ariana Wohl

Ages: 9–10

Grade: 5

Town: Northampton, Massachusetts

School: Jackson Street School

Goal: Protect trees in a local park

WHAT THEY DID

Summary

In 1989, the Northampton department of public works decided to cut down 12 full-grown trees in Childs Park to make a road wider and add parking spaces.

When Sarah and Kate heard the news, they told their friends Ariana and Laura about it.

All of them were concerned. Ariana pointed out that trees help keep our air clean. Sarah was concerned because animals like squirrels and birds would lose their homes. She says, "It was hard to imagine that one day there would be a park, and the next day there would be parking spaces."

The girls agreed: They had to stop the project; they would do whatever it took. Within days, they were staging a protest in front of the park.

Results

The park was saved, and the street was left as it was. And, Laura says, "I think a lot of the kids in this town have become more environmentally conscious as a result."

HOW THEY DID IT

1. They considered their options. Sarah's mother suggested they picket—hold up signs at the park—and they liked the idea. They also decided to write letters to the mayor and start a petition.

2. They made signs saying, "Save our trees, save our animals!" and "If you care, please honk your horn!"

3. They asked their friends to help picket, but they didn't let adults participate. "We wanted it to be strictly a kids' event," says Ariana. They called their group Community Children to Save Our Park (CCSOP).

4. They picketed for 2 days. Sarah says, "People were

very supportive: we got about 500 honks."

5. As a result of the picketing, the mayor came to Laura's house and met with the neighbors and protesters. Some people—like the engineer who did the plans for the wider street—opposed saving the park. He said, "An intersection is forever, a tree can always be planted again." But in the end, most people agreed with the kids.

YOU CAN BE A HERO

• "Don't be afraid to tell people what you think," says Laura. "One kid's father told us to wait until fall to picket. We said they were going to cut down the trees in two weeks, so we didn't want to take any chances."

• "Don't be afraid to tell the media what you're doing," says Laura. "I was scared to tell our local newspaper about our plans, because the article I'd read made it sound like the trees were already doomed. But the newspaper people aren't in charge. They just want news."

• How do you deal with the people who are against what you're doing? Laura says, "If they don't have much power, just ignore them. If they do, try to get someone more powerful on your side. In our case it was the mayor."

TONIGHT

Illustrated with *arpilleras* sewn by the Club de Madres Virgen del Carmen of Lima, Peru

IS CARNAVAL

BY ARTHUR DORROS

"Wake up, sleepyhead," my mother is calling. But I'm already awake. I'm thinking about Carnaval. This year I will play the *quena*, a flute, with my father in the band. "The quena is the voice of the band—the singer of the band," says Papa. Papa plays with the band every year at Carnaval. People in costumes will parade and dance to the music for three whole days and nights.

Carnaval is in the big village down the valley, and it's only three days away!

"We have a lot of work to do before then," Papa says. We work all year, almost every day, but not during Carnaval!

We get up each day before it is light outside, there is so much to do. Mama takes my little sister, Teresa, to the river to get water. Today Mama washes clothes, too. Papa and I look for firewood to use for cooking. Sometimes we walk a long way to find wood—there are hardly any trees in the high Andes Mountains of South America, where we live.

Today I bring my quena along, so I can practice special songs for Carnaval. A lot of the songs have a good beat that makes you want to dance. *Tunk tunk, tunk tunk.* Papa's ax chopping a log sounds like the beat of the *bombo*, the drum he will play with the band.

Back home Teresa drops kernels of corn into an empty pot. Mama will boil the corn for our meal. *Pling pling, pling pling pling.* The kernels make sounds like the strings of Uncle Pablo's *charango*. He will play in the band with us too, at Carnaval.

After our meal, we get a field ready for planting. I lead the oxen, to make sure they plow straight. Mama follows us and picks stones out of the loose earth. After Carnaval, my friend Paco and his family will help us plant potatoes. Sometimes Paco's family helps us in our field, and other times we help them in theirs. One of the songs I'm practicing for Carnaval is about working in the fields with friends.

After we plow, I take the hungry llamas high into the mountains to find grass. The best grass is by the crumbling walls of buildings made hundreds of years ago when the Incas ruled these mountains. No one knows how the giant stones were cut to fit together so well. Sometimes we use the old stones to build walls and houses and even terraces for the fields.

I sit on a wall and play my quena. I play a song called *"Mis Llamitas,"* "My Little Llamas," and the llamas leap and dance around. I imagine they are dancing to my music.

The wind whistling across the stones sounds like the windy notes of a *zampoña*, a panpipe. I will play my quena and Paco will play his zampoña when we meet at Carnaval. That's one of the things I like about Carnaval—we get together with friends from our mountain and from all around the valley.

One day is gone. Now we have only today and tomorrow before tomorrow night—when Carnaval begins. I can hardly wait. This morning Papa shears wool from an alpaca. An alpaca is like a llama, but with softer wool. I carry the wool to Mama, so she can spin it into yarn. "You don't have to run," laughs Mama. "Carnaval will come as soon as it can."

Mama's fingers twirl the wool round and round. She can spin yarn while she's walking, or selling vegetables, or doing almost anything. When she has enough yarn, she'll color it with different dyes. Grandma will weave it into cloth of many colors. Then Mama will cut and sew the cloth to make us clothes. Maybe she'll make me a new jacket.

In the afternoon, we dig potatoes out of the damp earth in a field we planted months ago. The digging usually makes me tired, but today I keep working as fast as I can to help harvest all the potatoes. Tomorrow we'll take them down into the valley to sell at the market. And after the market is cleared away, Carnaval will begin!

We gather red potatoes; yellow, black, and brown potatoes; even purple potatoes. In the Andes, we have hundreds of different kinds of potatoes.

We drop our potatoes into burlap bags, *plonk, plonk, plonk.* The llamas help carry the heavy bags to Antonio's truck. Antonio came from the village today, and he will sleep tonight in his truck.

Finally. Today we take the potatoes to market—then tonight is Carnaval!

I wait and wait to hear the truck start. The motor coughs and groans, *errr errr errr.* But at last Antonio gets it started. Mama, Papa, Teresa, and I—and the potatoes—bounce along in the back of the old truck, which rattles and shakes down the mountain. It stops like a bus to pick up people carrying onions, beans, carrots, turnips, peas, and peppers; llama wool; clothes; and food they have made for Carnaval.

"Hey," I hear someone say, "don't let that chicken eat our corn. We're taking it to market."

The truck bounces over a big bump. I reach down to make sure my quena is not broken. I want people to hear my quena sing when I play at Carnaval.

"Watch out flying over those bumps, Antonio," someone shouts. "Will this old truck fly us to the village?"

"Don't worry," Antonio shouts back. "This old truck and I know how to get there."

People hug when they climb into the truck. We don't see these friends very often. We all stand and look out along the way. People throw water balloons and water from buckets to try to splash us. They're excited about Carnaval.

At the market, I help unload the heavy bags of potatoes, and then I walk around. I love to see the brightly colored piles of vegetables. People trade wool that still smells like llamas or sheep. And the nutty smell of toasted fava beans and corn makes my mouth water.

But today I can't wait until Mama sells all of our potatoes and the market is cleared away. Then people will come out in their costumes. At first it will be hard to see who each person is—many of the people will be wearing masks. I'll find the band. Papa's bombo will start booming, Paco's zampoña will be whistling, and Uncle Pablo's charango plinging. People will start shouting "Play your songs," stamping their feet, swirling, turning, dancing to the music faster and faster because—

TONIGHT IS CARNAVAL.

When I play my quena with the band, people start to sing. My quena sings and the people sing. I play the special songs I've learned for Carnaval, about llamas, mountains, and friends. We play songs with a beat for dancing. Paco and I watch all the people hold onto each other in one long line that dances—laughing, winding through the village.

Our band plays under the moon and flickering stars, and we will play until the sun comes up. We play the songs of our mountain days and nights . . . for tonight is Carnaval.

HOW ARPILLERAS ARE MADE

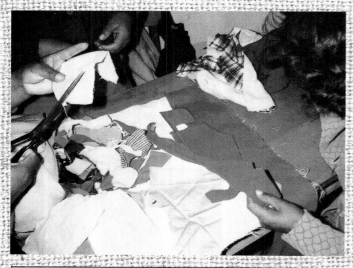

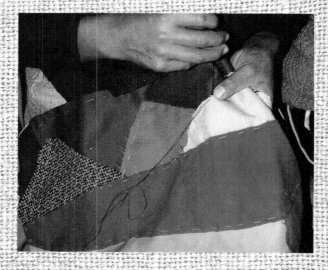

An arpillera-maker draws the design on white cloth. Pieces of cloth are selected and cut to fit the design.

Big pieces of cloth are sewn on to form the background.

The edges of each shape are neatly stitched, and details are added by sewing on more pieces of cut cloth and by embroidering.

Dolls and other three-dimensional objects (vegetables, musical instruments) are made . . .

Another arpillera is finished.

. . . and sewn onto the arpillera.

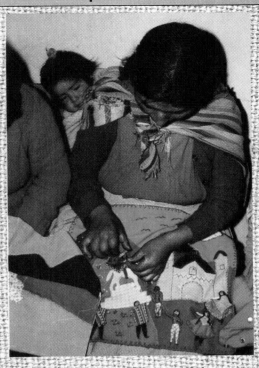

Arpillera-makers often work together in groups. These members of the Club de Madres Virgen del Carmen are making vegetables and dolls for arpilleras. With money from the sale of arpilleras, the group also runs a kitchen that helps feed two to three hundred people a day.

CARNIVAL

In 1885, a newspaper reporter was visiting Saint Paul, Minnesota. He took one look at all the snow, felt the icy wind blowing, and wrote, "No right-minded person would ever come here in the winter!" The people of Saint Paul decided to prove that reporter wrong. Every winter, MILLIONS of visitors flock to the snowy city. What's the attraction? Saint Paul's Winter Carnival, of course! It's the nation's oldest winter carnival, first held in 1886. And it's so much fun that no one even notices the cold!

The giant ice palace is always a favorite with Winter Carnival visitors. It took several weeks and 30,000 huge blocks of ice to build this sparkling castle.

IN THE SNOW

▲ Even a reindeer visited Saint Paul's first Winter Carnival in 1886.

119

Each year, a new Winter Carnival button is the ticket to all the fun.

The Legend of the Winter Carnival

A long, long time ago, Boreas, King of all the Winds, discovered Saint Paul—a beautiful ice-covered city in Minnesota. "This frozen wonderland will be my winter capital!" he declared. To celebrate, King Boreas and his queen held a winter carnival in their new home. There were twelve days of feasting and fun for everyone.

But not everyone was happy about the celebration. Boreas's enemy, Vulcanus, King of Fire, hated ice and snow. "Away with winter!" he bellowed. "It's time for spring!"

Vulcanus and his followers plotted to drive King Boreas out of Saint Paul. On the last day of the carnival, Vulcanus stormed into the Boreas's ice castle. To keep the peace, King Boreas agreed to leave. And so the warmth of springtime returned to Saint Paul. However, each year Boreas returns, and he brings another winter carnival with him!

▲ Speedskating is just one of the fun winter sports that take place during the Winter Carnival.

▲ Artists use chainsaws and chisels to create fantastic ice carvings. Over a million people brave the cold weather each year to see the frozen sculptures.

▲ From late January to early February, glistening ice sculptures turn downtown Saint Paul into a winter wonderland.

PROJECT

How to Create a Community Quilt

Design a quilt *that tells* all about *your community.*

Have you ever seen a community quilt? It's a special patchwork wall hanging that celebrates the good things about a community. On a community quilt you may see pictures of famous landmarks, community events, beautiful parks, or important people. You may even find words written on it. Many of these special quilts are beautiful works of art. But they also show why communities are great places to live.

Keith
Age 8

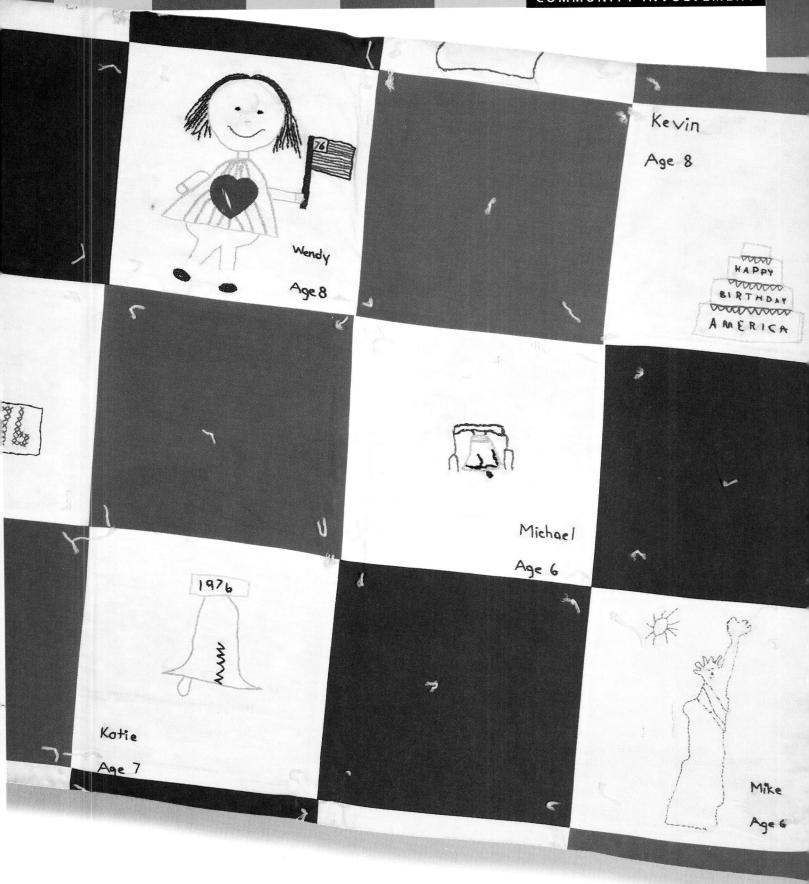

Wendy
Age 8

Kevin
Age 8

HAPPY
BIRTHDAY
AMERICA

Michael
Age 6

1976

Katie
Age 7

Mike
Age 6

1 Choose a Subject

With your classmates, list the things that make your community unlike any other. These may include people, places, events, or activities. Choose the part of your community that you want to show on a quilt square.

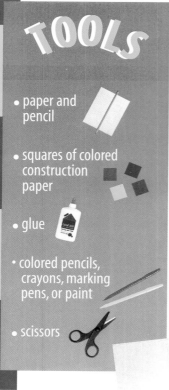

TOOLS

- paper and pencil
- squares of colored construction paper
- glue
- colored pencils, crayons, marking pens, or paint
- scissors

Special parts of your community might be:

- famous landmarks such as statues or buildings
- city, state, or national parks
- community groups
- places that people use, such as libraries or playfields
- celebrations and parades
- people, such as the mayor

2 | Research It

Find out something about the landmark, place, group, person, or activity you have chosen. You can look for information in your school or local library. You can talk to people who have lived in the community for a long time. You can call or write to your local chamber of commerce, too. If you are researching a place, you may be able to visit it. Take notes on the information you find.

Here are some questions you can ask about a landmark, place, or event:

- How long has it been in the community?
- What is it? What does it do?
- Why is it important?

Now you're ready to design your quilt square for your community quilt.

How Am I Doing?

Before you make your community quilt, take a few minutes and ask yourself these questions:

- Have I chosen a landmark, place, person, group, or activity that is important to my community?
- Have I found information about my choice?

3 Design Your Square

Decide what your quilt square will look like. On a sheet of construction paper, draw a picture of the person, group, landmark, place, or activity that you have researched.

Around the edges of the paper, glue on a border of a different colored paper. On your square, write the name of your choice. If you want, add an interesting fact about it. Write your name and age below your drawing or on the border.

Tip Make sure all the squares in your community quilt are the same size. That way, they will easily fit together.

4 Make a Quilt

With your classmates, glue all the quilt squares together. You may want to make several small quilts instead of one large one. Display your quilts on a classroom wall.

Then tell the class what you learned about your community. Answer any questions. Have a quilt party, too! Invite other classes in your school to see your community quilt.

If You Are Using a Computer ...

Work with your classmates to design your quilt on the computer. Use a graphics program that has a background grid. Use the Shape Tools to create individual panels. Then type or draw within the squares to show what will go where. Print out your work to use as a guide when you put the quilt together.

JULY 4th

Our Mayor

Town Hall

Sam Wada Age 7

PARADE

Mayor Jill Lobo

CONGRATULATIONS
You have learned how people improve their communities. What can you do to make your community a better place?

Lorka Muñoz
Community ▶

Glossary

ad·ver·tise·ments
(ad′vər tīz′mənts) *noun*
Public announcements that describe a product or service for sale. TV and radio commercials are advertisements. Advertisements are also found in newspapers and magazines.
▲ advertisement

al·pac·a
(al pak′ə) *noun*
An animal that has long silky brown or black wool. An alpaca looks like a llama.

au·di·enc·es
(ô′dē ən səz) *noun*
Groups of people gathered in a place to hear or see something.
▲ audience

bulg·ing
(bul′jing) *adjective*
Bursting at the seams or puffed out. That *bulging* suitcase is about to pop open.

bull·doz·er
(bŏŏl′dō′zər) *noun*
A tractor with a wide steel blade across the front. It is used to clear land and build roads.

bur·lap (bûr′lap) *noun*
A rough brown cloth. It is used for making bags and other things.

cam·pus
(kam′pəs) *noun*
The grounds and buildings of a school, such as a college.

bulldozer

cha·ran·go
(chə ran′gō) *noun*
An instrument with five strings from South America. A charango looks like a guitar.

crum•pled
(krum′pəld) *verb*
Crushed into a ball.
Karen *crumpled* the
paper in her hand.
▲ **crumple**

dem•on•stra•tion
(dem′ən strā′shən) *noun*
A gathering of many
people in public to
show how they feel
about something. We
held a *demonstration* to
save a playground.

dis•grace
(dis grās′) *noun*
Something that is
shameful. That old
broken-down house is
a *disgrace* to our
neighborhood.

dor•mi•to•ries
(dôr′mi tôr′ēz) *noun*
Places where many
people sleep. ▲ **dormitory**

el•e•men•ta•ry
(el′e men′tə rē) *adjective*
In school, having to do
with kindergarten through
grades four, five, or six.

ex•am•i•na•tions
(ig zam′ə nā′shəns)
noun
Close looks or
inspections.
▲ **examination**

for•eign
(fôr′in) *adjective*
From another country.
We cooked a dinner of
foreign foods.

gar•bage
(gär′bij) *noun*
Scraps of food and other
trash to be thrown away.

har•vest (här′vist) *verb*
To gather a crop when it
is ripe. Farmer Tompkins
will *harvest* her corn in
August.

haze (hāz) *noun*
Fine mist, smoke, or dust
in the air.

In•cas (ing′kəs) *noun*
Members of a Native
American people who
lived in the South
American country of Peru
before the Spanish
takeover in 1535. ▲ **Inca**

in•dus•tri•al
(in dus′trē əl) *adjective*
Having a large number
of businesses or factories.

a	add	o͝o	took	ə =		
ā	ace	o͞o	pool	a in *above*		
â	care	u	up	e in *sicken*		
ä	palm	û	burn	i in *possible*		
e	end	yo͞o	fuse	o in *melon*		
ē	equal	oi	oil	u in *circus*		
i	it	ou	pout			
ī	ice	ng	ring			
o	odd	th	thin			
ō	open	th	this			
ô	order	zh	vision			

Glossary

in·spec·tors
(in spek′tərz) *noun*
People who look over official papers with care. The *inspectors* looked at our passports when we arrived at the airport.
▲ **inspector**

lla·mas (lä′məz) *noun*
Animals from South America related to camels but are smaller and have no humps. Llamas carry heavy loads. Their wool is used for making cloth.
▲ **llama**

Fact File

• When a **llama** gets angry, it spits.
• Llamas have big eyes with long eyelashes that make them look cute.
• Llamas can live at very high places in mountains.

---

ma·chine
(mə shēn′) *noun*
A tool that has moving parts that work together to do a special job. A lawn mower is a *machine* that cuts grass.

me·di·a
(mē′dē ə) *noun*
All the ways of giving people news and entertainment. Radio, television, newspapers, and magazines are part of the *media*.

mi·grate (mī′grāt) *verb*
To move from one country to another. Many people from other countries *migrate* to America.

mire (mīr) *noun*
An area of muddy, wet, soft ground. After it rained, our car became stuck in the *mire*.

new·com·ers
(noō′kum′ərz) *noun*
People who have recently arrived in a place. Our neighbors in the blue house are *newcomers* from Pakistan.
▲ **newcomer**

par·ti·ci·pate
(pär tis′ə pāt′) *verb*
To be a part of an activity with others; to take part in something.

pe·ti·tion
(pə tish′ən) *noun*
A written statement that asks someone to do something. People who agree with the person making the statement sign the petition.

pro·grams
(prō′gramz) *noun*
Entertainment seen in theaters, on television, or heard on the radio. During the school year, we gave three musical *programs* for our parents.
▲ **program**

pro·tes·ters
(prō′tes tûrz) *noun*
People who speak out against an idea or decision. The *protesters* shouted at the men who want to tear up the town park. ▲ **protester**

re·cit·ed (ri sī′ted) *verb*
Spoke from memory in front of a group. Oscar *recited* some poems for his class. ▲ **recite**

re•pair (ri pâr´) *verb*
To fix something that is broken.

Thesaurus

repair
fix
mend

rub•bish (rub´ish) *noun*
Material to be thrown out; trash.

rust•y (rus´tē) *adjective*
Covered with rust. Rust is a reddish-brown coating that forms on iron or steel when it is wet for too long.

rusty

signs (sīnz) *noun*
Boards or cards covered with writing or pictures that give information.
▲ **sign**

slums (slumz) *noun*
Very poor and crowded areas in a city. ▲ **slum**

smog (smog) *noun*
A mixture of smoke and fog in the air.

Word Study

The word **smog** was made from two other words, *smoke* and *fog*. By putting the first two letters of *smoke* together with the last two letters of fog, you have a new word—**smog**.

smoke•stacks (smōk´staks´) *noun*
Tall chimneys or pipes that carry smoke away from a factory.
▲ **smokestack**

sup•port•ive (sə pôr´tiv) *adjective*
Helpful or encouraging. Bill is *supportive* of Mary's idea to change recess hours.

sur•veyed (sər vād´) *verb*
Asked for information or opinions from a number of people. The store manager *surveyed* his customers to find out whether they liked peas or carrots more.
▲ **survey**

teach•ers (tē´chərz) *noun*
People who teach in a school or college.
▲ **teacher**

ter•ra•ces (ter´əs əz) *noun*
Flat areas cut out of hills. People often plant flowers or vegetables on terraces. ▲ **terrace**

a	add	o͝o	took	ə =	
ā	ace	o͞o	pool		a in *above*
â	care	u	up		e in *sicken*
ä	palm	û	burn		i in *possible*
e	end	yo͞o	fuse		o in *melon*
ē	equal	oi	oil		u in *circus*
i	it	ou	pout		
ī	ice	ng	ring		
o	odd	th	thin		
ō	open	th	this		
ô	order	zh	vision		

Authors & Illustrators

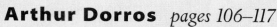

Arthur Dorros *pages 106–117*

This author/illustrator's career almost ended when he was in fifth grade. He had always loved to draw, but he often got frustrated with how his pictures came out. In high school, he started drawing again and hasn't stopped! Later he began writing his own books, too. Arthur Dorros spent a year living in South America. This experience led him to write his award-winning book *Tonight Is Carnaval*.

Lisa Campbell Ernst *pages 82–101*

Lisa Campbell Ernst says, "I have always loved animals, so of course I love to draw them." She notices animals wherever she goes, and many of her books also have animals in them. She was living in New York City when she got the idea for *Squirrel Park*.

Eloise Greenfield *pages 66–73*

Eloise Greenfield likes to listen to the sound of words. She hopes that her poems and books inspire others to have what she calls "word-madness." She also wants her books to provide "a true knowledge of Black heritage, including both the African and American experiences."

Ellen Levine *pages 56–65*

As a child, Ellen Levine loved to read. "A book could transport me to another time or place," she says. Now Ellen Levine writes books for young readers that transport them to other times and places. She interviewed hundreds of people and read many old journals and letters to collect the information she needed for . . . *If Your Name Was Changed at Ellis Island.*

Arnold Lobel *pages 10–19*

People often asked Arnold Lobel which of his many books was his favorite. He always gave the same answer. "My favorite is always the next one, the one I haven't done yet." Throughout his career as an author and illustrator, he worked on over 70 books. Arnold Lobel died in 1987.

Chris Van Allsburg *pages 22–45*

Chris Van Allsburg says, "The way to get good at something is by doing it a lot." When he was in elementary school, Van Allsburg liked art class so much he would go to school even when he was sick if he had art that day. Drawing was just a hobby for Chris Van Allsburg, until a friend suggested he try to illustrate a book. He's now one of the most popular author/illustrators in America. "I have a favorite kind of mood I like in my art," he says. "I like things to be mysterious."

Books &

Author/Illustrator Study

More by Chris Van Allsburg

Jumanji
A girl and her brother find that a new game leads them to an amazing adventure.

Two Bad Ants
Get an ant's-eye view of an ordinary home in this funny book.

The Wreck of the Zephyr
Something mysterious has happened to a ship, the *Zephyr*, and all of her crew.

Chris Van Allsburg

Fiction

The Best Town in the World
by Byrd Baylor
illustrated by Ronald Himler
Where is the best town in the world? What makes it so special? The boy in this story is sure he knows the answers.

The Village of Round and Square Houses
by Ann Grifalconi
An old African story explains why men live in square houses and women in round ones.

Yagua Days
by Cruz Martel
illustrated by
Jerry Pinkney
What's a yagua day? A New York City boy finds out when he visits his parents' hometown in Puerto Rico.

Nonfiction

Powwow
by George Ancona
What music! What dancing! What fun! Beautiful color photographs help capture the excitement of this Native American celebration.

Recycle! A Handbook for Kids
by Gail Gibbons
Are you part of a recycling project? There are lots of things you can do at home, at school, and in your community to help reuse materials.

The Town That Moved
by Mary Jane Finsand
When iron ore was discovered underneath their town, the people of Hibbing had to move. But they didn't move out of town. They took their town with them. Here is the amazing true story of how they did it.

&Media

 ## Videos

 ## Software

Magazines

The Butter Battle Book
Turner/Good Times
This animated retelling of Dr. Seuss's favorite book is about the best way to eat bread and butter. Because the Yooks and Zooks can't agree, they end up going to war! (30 minutes)

Koi and the Kola Nuts
Rabbit Ears
Koi sets out to find a new village—one where he will be treated as a king's son. Whoopi Goldberg narrates this wise and funny African tale. (30 minutes)

The Lone Star Kid
Public Media
Brian's town is going to elect a new mayor—and eleven-year-old Brian wants the job! This is based on a true story. (58 minutes)

SimCity
Maxis
(Macintosh Plus, IBM)
Where do the roads go? How tall should the buildings be? Design and run a city—all by yourself.

3-2-1 Contact
Children's Television Workshop
This science and technology magazine has stories, art, and photos. It includes articles about the environment and how technology helps communities solve problems.

U*S*Kids
Field Publications
Would you like to know more about the world around you? This magazine includes news, true-life stories, and information about the environment.

A Place to Write

Hannah Lindahl Children's Museum
1402 South Main Street
Mishawaka, IN 46454

This museum displays objects that show what life is like in Mishawaka and its sister city in Japan. Write for information about the museum and the sister-cities project.

Acknowledgments

Grateful acknowledgment is made to the following sources for permission to reprint from previously published material. The publisher has made diligent efforts to trace the ownership of all copyrighted material in this volume and believes that all necessary permissions have been secured. If any errors or omissions have inadvertently been made, proper corrections will gladly be made in future editions.

Front cover: Illustration from THE THREE LITTLE JAVELINAS by Susan Lowell. Illustration copyright © 1992 by Jim Harris. Published by Northland Publishing, Flagstaff, AZ. Used by permission.

Back cover: Top: *BABAR* from THE STORY OF BABAR by Jean de Brunhoff. Copyright © 1933 and renewed by Random House, Inc. Reprinted by permission of Random House, Inc. *BATMAN* image property of DC Comics. Used by permission. Batman is a trademark of DC Comics copyright © 1992. All rights reserved. *CLIFFORD* ® from CLIFFORD GETS A JOB by Norman Bridwell. Copyright © 1965 by Norman Bridwell. Reprinted by permission. CLIFFORD is a registered trademark of Norman Bridwell. *JULIAN* illustration from cover of MORE STORIES JULIAN TELLS by Ann Cameron. Illustration copyright © 1986 by Ann Strugnell. Reprinted by permission of Alfred A. Knopf, Inc. *KERMIT*: Kermit the Frog is copyrighted and used by special permission of Jim Henson Productions. *LASSIE* photograph by Daniel R. Westergren © National Geographic Society. Used by permission. *MS. FRIZZLE* illustration copyright © 1994 by Bruce Degen. Reprinted by permission. Middle: Cover by Robert Tannenbaum. Bottom: Cover by Margaret Cusak.

Acknowledgments

Grateful acknowledgment is made to the following sources for permission to reprint from previously published material. The publisher has made diligent efforts to trace the ownership of all copyrighted material in this volume and believes that all necessary permissions have been secured. If any errors or omissions have inadvertently been made, proper corrections will gladly be made in future editions.

Unit Opener: *BABAR:* Illustration from THE STORY OF BABAR by Jean de Brunhoff. Copyright © 1933 and renewed 1961 by Random House, Inc. Reprinted by permission of Random House, Inc. *BATMAN:* Batman image property of DC Comics. Used by permission. Batman is a trademark of DC Comics copyright © 1992. All rights reserved. *CLIFFORD:* Clifford® by Norman Bridwell from CLIFFORD GETS A JOB by Norman Bridwell. Copyright © 1965 by Norman Bridwell. Reprinted by permission. CLIFFORD is a registered trademark of Norman Bridwell. *JULIAN:* Cover illustration from MORE STORIES JULIAN TELLS by Ann Cameron, illustrated by Ann Strugnell. Illustration copyright © 1986 by Ann Strugnell. Reprinted by permission of Alfred A. Knopf, Inc. *KERMIT:* Kermit the Frog is copyrighted and used by special permission of Jim Henson Productions. *LASSIE:* Photograph by Daniel R. Westergren © National Geographic Society. Used by permission. *MS. FRIZZLE:* Illustration by Bruce Degen. Illustration copyright © 1994 by Bruce Degen. Reprinted by permission. THE MAGIC SCHOOL BUS is a registered trademark of Scholastic Inc.

Interior: *PETER RABBIT:* Illustration from THE TALE OF PETER RABBIT by Beatrix Potter. Copyright © 1902, 1987 by Frederick Warne & Co. Used by permission. *BOXCAR CHILDREN:* Cover illustration from THE MYSTERY OF THE HIDDEN PAINTING by Gertrude Chandler Warner. Cover illustration copyright © 1993 by Scholastic Inc. Reprinted by permission. THE BOXCAR CHILDREN is a registered trademark of Albert Whitman & Company. *MADELINE:* Illustration from MADELINE AND THE GYPSIES by Ludwig Bemelmans. Copyright © 1958, 1959 by Ludwig Bemelmans, renewed copyright © 1986, 1987 by Madeleine Bemelmans and Barbara Bemelmans. Used by permission of Viking Penguin, a division of Penguin Books USA Inc. *BATMAN:* Batman image property of DC Comics. Used by permission. Batman is a trademark of DC Comics copyright © 1992. All rights reserved. *LASSIE:* Photograph by Daniel R. Westergren © National Geographic Society. Used by permission. *RAMONA:* Illustration from RAMONA QUIMBY, AGE 8 by Beverly Cleary, illustrated by Alan Tiegreen. Copyright © 1981 by Beverly Cleary. Used by permission of Morrow Junior Books, a division of William Morrow & Company, Inc. *CHARLIE BROWN:* © 1950 United Feature Syndicate, Inc. Used by permission. *SNOOPY:* © 1958 United Feature Syndicate, Inc. Used by permission. *BABAR:* Illustration from THE STORY OF BABAR by Jean de Brunhoff. Copyright © 1933, renewed 1961 by Random House, Inc. Reprinted by permission of Random House, Inc. *CLIFFORD:* Illustration from CLIFFORD GETS A JOB by Norman Bridwell. Copyright © 1965 by Norman Bridwell. Reprinted by permission. CLIFFORD is a registered trademark of Norman Bridwell. *ENCYCLOPEDIA BROWN:*

Illustration from ENCYCLOPEDIA BROWN, BOY DETECTIVE by Donald J. Sobol. Copyright © 1963 by Donald J. Sobol. Used by permission of Lodestar Books, an affiliate of Dutton Children's Books, a division of Penguin USA Inc. *KERMIT:* Kermit the Frog is copyrighted and used by special permission of Jim Henson Productions. *CHAPULIN COLORADO:* Chapulin Colorado used by permission of Televisa, Mexico. *AMELIA BEDELIA:* character image from one illustration from PLAY BALL, AMELIA BEDELIA by Peggy Parish, illustration by Wallace Tripp. Illustrations copyright © 1972 by Wallace Tripp. Reprinted by permission of HarperCollins Publishers. *JULIAN:* Cover illustration from MORE STORIES JULIAN TELLS by Ann Cameron, illustrated by Ann Strugnell. Illustration copyright © 1986 by Ann Strugnell. Reprinted by permission of Alfred A. Knopf, Inc. *CARMEN SANDIEGO:* Where in the World is Carmen Sandiego?® is based on the computer games from Brøderbund Software, Inc. Where in the World is Carmen Sandiego?®, Carmen Sandiego™ and the logo design are trademarks of Brøderbund Software, Inc. Used with permission. *IKTOMI:* Illustration from IKTOMI AND THE BERRIES by Paul Goble. Copyright © 1989 by Paul Goble. Used by permission of Orchard Books, New York. *TIME WARP TRIO:* Illustration from YOUR MOTHER WAS A NEANDERTHAL by Jon Scieszka, illustrated by Lane Smith. Illustration copyright © 1993 by Lane Smith. Used by permission of Viking Penguin, a division of Penguin Books USA Inc. *MS. FRIZZLE:* Illustration from THE MAGIC SCHOOL BUS LOST IN THE SOLAR SYSTEM by Joanna Cole, illustrated by Bruce Degen. Illustration copyright © 1990 by Bruce Degen. Reprinted by permission of Scholastic Inc. THE MAGIC SCHOOL BUS is a registered trademark of Scholastic Inc. *BABY-SITTERS CLUB:* Cover illustration from THE BABY-SITTERS REMEMBER by Ann M. Martin. Cover illustration copyright © 1994 by Scholastic Inc. THE BABY-SITTERS CLUB is a registered trademark of Scholastic Inc. Reprinted by permission. "The Magic School Bus Hops Home" is an adaptation of a production script by Jocelyn Stevenson based on THE MAGIC SCHOOL BUS book series by Joanna Cole and Bruce Degen. Copyright © 1995 by Joanna Cole and Bruce Degen. All rights reserved. Used by permission. Major funding for Scholastic's THE MAGIC SCHOOL BUS television project is provided by Microsoft Home, makers of a broad line of quality software for your home computer. Additional funding is provided by U.S. Department of Energy and Carnegie Corporation of New York. Presented on PBS by SCETV. Book covers from THE MAGIC SCHOOL BUS series: THE MSB ON THE OCEAN FLOOR illustration copyright © 1992 by Bruce Degen. THE MSB LOST IN THE SOLAR SYSTEM illustration copyright © 1990 by Bruce Degen. THE MSB INSIDE THE HUMAN BODY illustration copyright © 1989 by Bruce Degen. THE MSB INSIDE THE EARTH illustration copyright © 1987 by Bruce Degen. THE MSB IN THE TIME OF THE DINOSAURS illustration copyright © 1994 by Bruce Degen. Reprinted by permission of Scholastic Inc. THE MAGIC SCHOOL BUS is a registered trademark of Scholastic Inc.

Illustrations of Ms. Frizzle (pp. 30-33) from THE MAGIC SCHOOL BUS LOST IN THE SOLAR SYSTEM by Joanna Cole, illustrated by Bruce Degen. Illustration copyright © 1990 by Bruce Degen. Reprinted by permission of Scholastic Inc.

Selection, cover, and logo from THE BABY-SITTERS CLUB #36: JESSI'S BABY-SITTER by Ann M. Martin, cover art by Hodges Soileau. Text copyright © 1990 by Ann M. Martin. Cover illustration © 1988 by Scholastic Inc. Book covers from THE BABY-SITTERS CLUB series: KRISTY'S GREAT IDEA cover illustration copyright © 1986 by Scholastic Inc. HELLO MALLORY cover illustration by Hodges Soileau. Illustration copyright © 1990 by Scholastic Inc. Reprinted by permission of Scholastic Inc. THE BABY-SITTERS CLUB and APPLE PAPERBACKS are registered trademarks of Scholastic Inc.

Selections and cover from INCREDIBLE MINI-BEASTS by Christopher Maynard. Photography by Frank Greenaway, Neil Fletcher, Jane Burton, Kim Taylor, Stephen Oliver and Colin Keates. Copyright © 1994 by Covent Garden Books Ltd. Book covers from INCREDIBLE LITTLE MONSTERS, INCREDIBLE FLYING MACHINES, and INCREDIBLE DINOSAURS, all by Christopher Maynard, copyright © 1994 by Covent Garden Books Ltd. Used by permission of Snapshot™, an imprint of Covent Garden Books and Elan Press (UK).

Selections and covers from I SPY: A BOOK OF PICTURE RIDDLES and I SPY FANTASY: A BOOK OF PICTURE RIDDLES. Photographs by Walter Wick, riddles by Jean Marzollo. I SPY: A BOOK OF PICTURE RIDDLES text copyright © 1992 by Jean Marzollo. Illustrations and photographs copyright © 1992 by Walter Wick. I SPY FANTASY text copyright © 1994 by Jean Marzollo. Illustrations and photographs copyright © 1994 by Walter Wick. Book cover from I SPY CHRISTMAS, illustrations and photographs copyright © 1992 by Walter Wick. Book covers from I SPY MYSTERY and I SPY FUNHOUSE, photographs copyright © 1993 by Walter Wick. Reprinted by permission of Scholastic Inc. I SPY is a registered trademark of Scholastic Inc.

"The Case of the Runaway Elephant" and cover from ENCYCLOPEDIA BROWN LENDS A HAND by Donald J. Sobol, illustrated by Leonard Shortall. Text copyright © 1974 by Donald J. Sobol. Illustrations copyright © 1974 by Thomas Nelson, Inc. Used by permission of Lodestar Books, an affiliate of Dutton Children's Books, a division of Penguin USA Inc. Illustrations on pp. 68, 73, and 76 by Leonard Shortall from ENCYCLOPEDIA BROWN, BOY DETECTIVE by Donald J. Sobol. Copyright © 1963 by Donald J. Sobol. Book covers from ENCYCLOPEDIA BROWN, BOY DETECTIVE and ENCYCLOPEDIA BROWN TRACKS THEM DOWN, cover illustrations copyright © 1982 by Dick Williams. Used by permission of Lodestar Books, an affiliate of Dutton Children's Books, a division of Penguin USA Inc. Book covers from ENCYCLOPEDIA BROWN KEEPS THE PEACE and ENCYCLOPEDIA BROWN GETS HIS MAN, cover illustrations copyright © 1982 by Dick Williams. Reprinted by permission of Bantam Books, a division of Bantam Doubleday Dell Publishing Group, Inc. Book covers from ENCYCLOPEDIA BROWN CARRIES ON and ENCYCLOPEDIA BROWN SETS THE PACE, cover illustrations copyright © 1982 by Scholastic Inc. APPLE PAPERBACKS is a registered trademark of Scholastic Inc.

Selections and cover from 101 ELEPHANT JOKES compiled by Robert Blake. Copyright © 1964 by Scholastic Inc. Used by permission.

Illustrations and logo of Carmen Sandiego are used by permission of Brøderbund. Where in the World is Carmen Sandiego?® is based on the computer games from Brøderbund Software, Inc. Where in the

Photography and Illustration Credits

Acknowledgments

Grateful acknowledgment is made to the following sources for permission to reprint from previously published material. The publisher has made diligent efforts to trace the ownership of all copyrighted material in this volume and believes that all necessary permissions have been secured. If any errors or omissions have inadvertently been made, proper corrections will gladly be made in future editions.

Unit Opener: Robert Tannenbaum.

Interior: "Home Place" from HOME PLACE by Crescent Dragonwagon, with illustrations by Jerry Pinkney. Text copyright © 1990 by Crescent Dragonwagon. Illustrations copyright © 1990 by Jerry Pinkney. This edition is reprinted by arrangement with Atheneum Books for Young Readers, Simon & Schuster Children's Publishing Division.

"Meet the Dirt Detectives" by Sheila Fairley reprinted with the permission of the publisher, OWL Magazine. OWL™ The Discovery Magazine for Children is published by The Young Naturalist Foundation. Logo used by permission. OWL and logo are trademarks of the Young Naturalist Foundation.

"Sunken Treasure" from SUNKEN TREASURE by Gail Gibbons. Copyright © 1988 by Gail Gibbons. Reprinted by permission of HarperCollins Publishers.

Photo of Armor of George Clifford, copyright ©1932 by The Metropolitan Museum of Art, New York (Munsey Fund, 1932, 32.130.6). "How to Create an Artifact Exhibit Card" text adaptation from INSIDE THE MUSEUM: A CHILDREN'S GUIDE TO THE METROPOLITAN MUSEUM OF ART by Joy Richardson. Published in 1993 by The Metropolitan Museum of Art, New York, and Harry N. Abrams, Incorporated, New York. Used by permission.

Selection and cover from PUEBLO STORYTELLER by Diane Hoyt-Goldsmith, illustrated by Lawrence Migdale. Text copyright © 1991 by Diane Hoyt-Goldsmith, photographs copyright © 1991 by Lawrence Migdale. Reprinted by permission of Holiday House, Inc.

Selection and cover from WILD AND WOOLLY MAMMOTHS by Aliki. Copyright © 1977 by Aliki Brandenberg. Reprinted by permission of HarperCollins Publishers.

"My Father's Grandfather and the Time Machine" by Staton Rabin. First published in Cricket Magazine. Copyright © 1991 by Staton Rabin. Reprinted by permission of the author. Cricket logo used by permission of Carus Publishing Company.

"The Fun They Had" by Isaac Asimov, adapted by Dwight Jon Zimmerman, illustrated by Evan Dorkin, from THE BANK STREET BOOK OF SCIENCE FICTION. Copyright © 1951 by NEA Service, Inc., copyright © 1989 by Byron Preiss Visual Publications, Inc. Cover illustration copyright © 1989 by Byron Preiss Visual Publications, Inc. Reprinted by permission.

"Kids Predict the Future" in Scholastic News, January 5, 1990. Copyright © 1990 by Scholastic Inc. Reprinted by permission.

Cover of FREDERICK DOUGLASS FIGHTS FOR FREEDOM by Margaret Davidson. Illustration copyright © 1968 by Scholastic Inc. Published by Scholastic Inc.

Cover of GEORGE WASHINGTON'S BREAKFAST by Jean Fritz, illustrated by Paul Galdone. Illustration copyright © 1969 by Paul Galdone. Published by Coward-McCann, Inc.

Cover from LET'S GO TRAVELING by Robin Rector Krupp. Illustrations copyright © 1992 by Robin Rector Krupp. Published by William Morrow & Company, Inc.

Cover of THREE NAMES by Patricia MacLachlan, illustrated by Alexander Pertzoff. Illustration copyright © 1991 by Alexander Pertzoff. Published by HarperCollins Publishers.

Photography and Illustration Credits

Photos: © John Lei for Scholastic Inc, all Tool Box items unless otherwise noted. p. 2 tl, cl: © Frank Cruz for Scholastic Inc.; shovel: © Richard Megna/Fundamental Photos for Scholastic Inc. pp. 2-3: © Frank Cruz for Scholastic Inc. p. 3 bc: © Frank Cruz for Scholastic Inc. p. 4 c: Ana Esperanza Nance for Scholastic Inc.; tc: © Telegraph Colour Library/FPG International Corp. p. 4 bl: Frank Cruz for Scholastic Inc. p. 5 c: Ana Esperanza Nance for Scholastic Inc.; tc: © FPG International Corp. p. 6 tc: © FPG International Corp.; c: © Ana Esperanza Nance for Scholastic Inc. p. 24-25: Nicholas Leibrecht; inset Courtesy of Mrs. George Williamson. p. 26: Nicholas Leibrecht. p. 27: Leif Peng. p. 28 cl: © Telegraph Colour Library/FPG International Corp.; all others: © Frank Cruz for Scholastic Inc. pp. 28-29: © Frank Cruz for Scholastic Inc. p. 29 c: © Frank Cruz for Scholastic Inc.; tr: © John Running; br: © David Waitz for Scholastic Inc. p. 30 all: © Frank Cruz for Scholastic Inc. p. 31 bl: © Keith Kent/Science Photo Library/Photo Researchers, Inc.; cr: © Frank Cruz for Scholastic Inc. p. 54 bl: © John Lei for Scholastic Inc.; bc: © Stanley Bach for Scholastic Inc. p. 55 br: © Frank Cruz for Scholastic Inc.; all others: © John Lei for Scholastic Inc. p. 58 br: © Deutshes Museum Munich. p. 59 cl: © Buffalo Bill Historical Center.; tr: © USC McKissick Columbia Photo; br: © All rights reserved McKissick Museum, The University of South Carolina. p. 60 cl: © Halley Ganges for Scholastic Inc.; br: © Ancient Art and Architecture Collection. p. 61 tl: © The Bettmann Archive; tr: © STB/Still Moving Picture Co.; br: © Scottish National Portrait Gallery. p. 62 tl, bc: © British Museum; tr: © Wyoming State Museum. p. 63 tl: © Museum of the City of New York; br: © American Philosophical Society. p. 64 tl: © Chris Luneski/Image Cascade; bl: © The Art Museum, Princeton University, Gift of the Arthur M. Sackler Foundation; cr: © Culver Pictures. p. 65 tl: © Smithsonian Institution, Washington D.C.; br: New York Times/Ana Esperanza Nance for Scholastic Inc. p. 66 tl, bl: © Stephen Trimble/Courtesy The Heard Museum; cr: © The Lincoln Museum, Fort Wayne, IN; br: © Lloyd Ostendorf Collection, Dayton ,OH. p. 67 cl, bl: © "Bird of Paradise" quilt top c.1860. Collection of the Museum of American Folk Art, New York; Gift of the trustees of the Museum of American Folk Art 1979.7.1 Bride's Quilt and detail; cr: © Art Resource, N.Y. p. 68 tl: © Portable Sundial, Silver and Gold, 10th Century (d). Canterbury Cathedral, Canterbury, Kent/Bridgeman Art Library, London; cr: National Museum of American History, book published by Harry N. Abrams Inc. p. 69 tl: © M. Renaudeau/ Agence Hoa-Qui; bl: © Lee Boltin/Boltin Picture Library; tr: © The Science Museum/Science and Society Picture Library. p. 70 bl: © Shelburne Museum; tr: © Margarete Busing/Bildarchiv Preussischer Kalturbesitz. p. 71 cl, bl: © The Mexican Museum, San Francisco, CA., The Rockefeller Collection; tr: © Phil Johnson Ruth. p. 73 c: © Lawrence Migdale. p. 74 tl: © Lawrence Migdale. p. 75: © Jay Brousseau/The Image Bank. pp. 76-77: © Jay Brousseau/The Image Bank. p. 77: © Jay Brousseau/The Image Bank. p. 78: © Jay Brousseau/The Image Bank. p. 79 bc: © Lawrence Migdale. pp. 80-81 c: Courtesy Denver Public Library, Western History Department. p. 82: framed picture: © John Lei for Scholastic Inc.; br: © Stanley Bach for Scholastic Inc. p. 83 br: © Frank Cruz for Scholastic Inc. pp. 86-95: © Letraset/Kirchoff/Wohlberg Inc. p. 113 c: © Superstock, Inc. pp. 114-115 c: © John Lei for Scholastic Inc. p. 116 bl: © John Lei for Scholastic Inc. p. 117 bl, cr: Stanley Bach for Scholastic Inc.; bc: © John Lei for Scholastic Inc. p. 118 cl: © John Lei for Scholastic Inc.; br, bc: © Stanley Bach for Scholastic Inc. p. 119 cl, tr: © John Lei for Scholastic Inc.; br: © Frank Cruz for Scholastic Inc. p. 120 cr: © D. Cavagnero/Peter Arnold, Inc. p. 122 br: © George Lepp/Comstock. p. 123 bl: © Jane Grushow/Grant Heilman. p. 124 tl: Courtesy HarperCollins. p. 125 tr: Courtesy Holiday House. p. 127 br: © Stephen Ogilvy for Scholastic Inc.; bl: © John Gilmore/The Stock Market.

Illustrations: pp. 8-9, 56-57, 84-85: William Silvers; pp. 97-98, 100-102: Gail Piazza; pp. 104-112: Evan Dorkin.

Acknowledgments

Grateful acknowledgment is made to the following sources for permission to reprint from perviously published material. The publisher has made diligent efforts to trace the ownership of all copyrighted material in this volume and believes that all necessary permissions have been secured. If any errors or omissions have inadvertently been made, proper corrections will gladly be made in future editions.

Unit Opener: Margaret Cusak.

Interior: "On the Day Peter Stuyvesant Sailed Into Town" from ON THE DAY PETER STUYVESANT SAILED INTO TOWN by Arnold Lobel. Copyright © 1971 by Arnold Lobel. Reprinted by permission of HarperCollins Publishers.

"How Pittsburgh Cleaned Up" and cover from SCHOLASTIC ENVIRONMENTAL ATLAS OF THE UNITED STATES by Mark Mattson, map by Christopher Salvatico. Copyright © 1993 by Scholastic Inc. Reprinted by permission.

"Just a Dream" from JUST A DREAM by Chris Van Allsburg. Copyright © 1990 by Chris Van Allsburg. Reprinted by permission of Houghton Mifflin Co. All rights reserved.

"Linden Heights Neighborhood Vegetable Garden" poster from Park District Dayton-Montgomery County's Grow With Your Neighbors Program. Used by permission.

Selections and cover from IF YOUR NAME WAS CHANGED AT ELLIS ISLAND by Ellen Levine, illustrated by Wayne Parmenter. Text copyright © 1993 by Ellen Levine. Illustrations copyright © 1993 by Scholastic Inc. Reprinted by permission of Scholastic Inc.

Selection and cover from MARY McLEOD BETHUNE by Eloise Greenfield, illustrated by Jerry Pinkney. Text copyright © 1977 by Eloise Greenfield. Illustrations copyright © 1977 by Jerry Pinkney. Reprinted by permission of HarperCollins Publishers.

"Family Biscuits" recipe from THE BLACK FAMILY REUNION COOKBOOK, copyright © 1991 by The National Council of Negro Women, Inc. Used by permission of Tradery House, an imprint of The Wimmer Companies, Inc. of Memphis, TN.

"Squirrel Park" from SQUIRREL PARK by Lisa Campbell Ernst. Copyright © 1993 by Lisa Campbell Ernst. This edition is reprinted by arrangement with Simon & Schuster Books for Young Readers, Simon & Schuster Children's Publishing Division.

"Protecting a Park" and cover from KID HEROES OF THE ENVIRONMENT ($4.95) copyright © 1991, by The EarthWorks Group. Cover illustration by Steve Purcell. Published by EarthWorks Press, Berkeley, CA. Used with permission.

"Tonight Is Carnaval" from TONIGHT IS CARNAVAL by Arthur Dorros. Text copyright © 1991 by Arthur Dorros. Illustrations copyright © 1991 by Dutton Children's Books. Used by permission of Dutton Children's Books, a division of Penguin Books USA Inc.

Source logo from "Carnival in the Snow" used by permission of Saint Paul Festival and Heritage Foundation.

Cover from CITY GREEN by DyAnne DiSalvo-Ryan. Illustration copyright © 1994 by DyAnne DiSalvo-Ryan. Published by William Morrow & Company, Inc.

Cover from CLOUDY WITH A CHANCE OF MEATBALLS by Judi Barrett, drawn by Ron Barrett. Drawing copyright © 1978 by Ron Barrett. Published by Atheneum Books for Young Readers, Simon & Schuster Children's Publishing Division.

Cover from LILY AND MISS LIBERTY by Carla Stevens, illustrated by Deborah Kogan Ray. Illustration copyright © 1992 by Deborah Kogan Ray. Published by Scholastic Inc.

Cover from SAMUEL'S CHOICE by Richard Berleth, illustrated by James Watling. Illustration copyright © 1990 by James Watling. Published by Albert Whitman & Company.

Photography and Illustration Credits

Photos: © John Lei for Scholastic Inc. all Tool Box items unless otherwise noted. p. 2 bl: © John Lei for Scholastic Inc.; cl: © John Bessler for Scholastic Inc.; tl: © Dennie Eagleson for Scholastic Inc. pp. 2-3 background: Dennie Eagleson for Scholastic Inc. p. 3 br: © Dennie Eagleson for Scholastic Inc.; tc: © F. Stuart Westmorland/Photo Researchers. p. 4 c: © Francis Clark Westfield for Scholastic Inc.; tc: © F. Stuart Westmorland/Photo Researchers, Inc. p. 5 c: © Ana Esperanza Nance for Scholastic Inc.; tc: © F. Stuart Westmorland/Photo Researchers, Inc. p. 6 c: © Ana Esperanza Nance for Scholastic Inc.; tc: © F. Stuart Westmorland/Photo Researchers, Inc. p. 20 cl, cr: © Carnegie Library of Pittsburgh. p. 46 bl, hand: © Ken Frick for Scholastic Inc.; © F. Stuart Westmorland/Photo Researchers, Inc.; all others: © Lorka Munoz/Wegerzyn Horticultural Center, OH. p. 47 cr: © Leonard Rue III/Photo Researchers, Inc.; all others: © Dennie Eagleson for Scholastic Inc. p. 48 bl: © Dennie Eagleson for Scholastic Inc.; cr: © Lorka Muñoz; bc: © Grant Huntington for Scholastic Inc. p. 49 cr: © Dennie Eagleson for Scholastic Inc.; tc: © David S. Waitz for Scholastic Inc. pp. 50-51 c: © John Lei for Scholastic Inc. p. 52 br: © Stanley Bach for Scholastic Inc.; bl: © Call/West Stock. p. 53 bl, tr: © John Lei for Scholastic Inc. p. 53 br: © Dennis Eagleson for Scholastic Inc. p. 54-55 c: © "Pot Luck" quilt by Cochran. p. 74 cr: © Catherine Baumann for Scholastic Inc. p. 75 bc: © Ed Quinn/NYT Pictures. pp. 76-77 all: © John Lei for Scholastic Inc. p. 78 bc, br: © Stanley Bach for Scholastic Inc. p. 78-79 bc, tc, tr: © John Lei for Scholastic Inc. p. 79 br: © Dennis Eagleson for Scholastic Inc. pp. 80-81 c: © "Homebody" quilt by Sally A. Sellers. pp. 102-103 c: © The Tennessean. pp. 106-117 background: © Richard Megna/Fundamental Photographs for Scholastic Inc. pp. 118-119 c: © Greg Ryan/Sally Beyer/Minnesota Office of Tourism. p. 119 tr: © Wintertainment Foundation of the St. Paul Festival & Heritage Foundation. p. 120 tl: © Ken Karp for Scholastic Inc.; cr: © Richard Megna/ Fundamental Photographs for Scholastic Inc.; br: © Greg Ryan/Sally Beyer. p. 121 tc: © Ken Karp for Scholastic Inc.; cr: © Minnesota Office of Tourism. p. 121 bl: © Greg Ryan/Sally Beyer. pp. 122-123 c: © John Lei for Scholastic Inc. p. 124 br: © Bob Burch/Bruce Coleman, Inc.; bl: © Larry Tackett/Tom Stack & Associates. p. 125 tr: © Sylvain Grandadam/Tony Stone Images; cr: © Stanley Bach for Scholastic Inc. pp. 126-127 c: © Stanley Bach for Scholastic Inc. p. 127 br: © Dennis Eagleson for Scholastic Inc. p. 128 cr: © Derek Redfearn/The Image Bank. p. 131 bc: © Guido Alberto Rossi/The Image Bank. p. 132 tl: Courtesy of Scholastic Trade Department; cl: © Courtesy of Simon & Schuster. p. 133 tr: © Courtesy of Scholastic Trade Department; cr: © Courtesy of Scholastic Photo Library; br: © Houghton Miffin, Chris Van Allsburg. p. 135 bc: © Porterfield/Chickering/Photo Researchers, Inc.; c: © Patrick Donehue/Photo Researchers, Inc. p. 136 br: © Stephen Ogilvy for Scholastic Inc.

Illustrations: pp. 8-9: Margaret Cusack.